pocket
cornwall

Cornish Mines:
St Just to Redruth

Barry Gamble

Alison Hodge

Dedication
To my family: Caroline, Danica and Hal

First published in 2011 by
Alison Hodge, 2 Clarence Place,
Penzance, Cornwall TR18 2QA, UK
info@alison-hodge.co.uk
www.alisonhodgepublishers.co.uk

Reprinted 2013

Acknowledgements
I would like to thank Paul Richards, of Brea,
for checking the text and making useful
suggestions.

ISBN-13 978-0-906720-81-3

British Library Cataloguing-in-Publication Data
A catalogue record for this book is available from
the British Library.

Designed and originated by
BDP – Book Development and Production,
Penzance, Cornwall

Printed in China

Title page: Lyle's Shaft, North Wheal Basset,
Camborne-Redruth Mining District

Many of the sites described in this book
take in spectacular features but also include
areas containing open mine shafts, ruined
buildings and high cliffs. Please take care
not to place yourself or others at risk while
enjoying the landscape.

St Just Mining District

Levant Mine

OS Explorer 102: SW368346

The widespread surface remains of Levant Mine are located on the cliffs 2 miles north of St Just, about 600 yd west of Geevor Mine. A walk along this spectacular stretch of Atlantic coast reveals a range of fascinating archaeology of this famous old mine, made infamous by the accident that happened in 1919. It includes the Levant whim, Cornwall's oldest surviving beam engine, now in the care of the NT and brought back to working (steaming) order. The SWCP accesses the best of what there is to see; there is a car-park near the engine houses. The Trewellard Arms Hotel is nearby; there is an excellent café at Geevor Mine, or there are good pubs beside the B3306 in nearby Pendeen – either the North Inn or the Radjel.

Levant Mine was reworked by Geevor Mine, the first time a mine has ever been reclaimed from the sea.

The earliest reference to mining on the sett dates to 1670, but it is not until 1748

Decorative banded brickwork of the Levant man-engine stack. Originally, the steam engine that drove the man-engine in Daubuz's Shaft (later renamed Man-engine Shaft) was a 20-in rotative beam-whim installed in 1857. In 1893, this was replaced by a compound engine (18- and 30-in cylinders), the bed of which can be seen in the foreground. Man-engine Shaft, 40 yd to the NE, was recollared in 2003, and the tunnel from the miners' dry reopened. To glimpse the depths of the shaft from within the tunnel is a sombre experience.

Submarine workings were extended for a mile distant from the cliffs at a depth which reached over 300 fm below the sea-bed. Two surviving engine houses cluster around the mine's principal shafts, Skip and Engine, sunk little more than 50 ft from each other, as close to Levant Zawn and the rich undersea workings as was possible. The smaller, roofed, engine house, aligned with the older Skip Shaft, contains an all-indoor beam-whim, the oldest surviving Cornish engine (1840, Harvey's of Hayle 24-in to the design of Francis Michell), saved from scrap in 1935 and brought back to steam in the 1980s by the Trevithick Society. The larger engine house on the right was built in 1835, and contained a 40-in (later 45-in) Harvey's of Hayle pumping engine which served Engine Shaft.

that the name 'Levant' appears on *Martyn's Map*. Beginning as an amalgamation of small ventures such as Boscregan and Wheal Unity,

Levant Mine, which became distinguished as one of Cornwall's top ten champion mines, emerged in 1820. Its founding adventurers

Trewellard North Cliff: the remains of at least two phases of tin floors occupy the sloping ground to the left of the SWCP which runs from top left to bottom right in the photograph. The mine's arsenic works occupy the seaward side of the SWCP, and were built to produce arsenic as a by-product of calcining the tin concentrates.

Silty waste is stained red from iron oxide, hematite, which was intimately mixed with the ore; this natural pigment was mostly carried off in the dressing water discharged into the cove, causing a ruddy plume in the sea, a feature off this coast until Geevor finally closed in 1990. Levant practised the 'primitive' Cornish method of tin dressing, of sending stamped ore straight to buddles until a new mill was installed in 1921/2. A tramway embankment leads to the upstanding rank

of pillars (centre left) that formerly supported the roof of this mill which contained more advanced tin-dressing equipment. The rectangular channeled 'slime' pits (bottom right) collected fine tin otherwise lost to tin-streamers, or the sea.

The mine's arsenic works were built to produce arsenic as a by-product of calcining the tin concentrates. Condensing chambers and a flue, now buried, led from a row of four calciners (centre right) to the stack (top left). In 50 years from 1854, the mine produced nearly 4,000 tons of crude arsenic, and over 100 tons of crude arsenic continued to be produced annually until the 1920s when a new refinery was added, whereby the soot was recalcined to produce snow-white crystalline arsenic trioxide.

The foreground is a miners' bath, one of four in what was a state-of-the-art miners' dry or changing room, built in 1889. To the right of the photo (out of shot) is a spiral stairwell with granite steps that descend to a tunnel which accesses Man-engine Shaft; it has been reopened and conserved by the NT for public access, a memorial to one of Cornwall's worst mining disasters.

Stacks (right to left) belong to compressor/power house, stamps-engine and calciners. The compressor house (later, 1921, became a power house) dates from 1901, and enabled extra productivity to be gained from the increased use of rock drills and of the compressed-air winding engine at New Submarine Shaft installed in 1897 (Old Submarine Shaft, remarkably, had a steam hoist installed in the 210-fm level). No doubt the productivity of miners was also enhanced by assisting the ventilation in workings that were up to 350 fm deep, hot (typically 100°F), and up to a mile out under the sea, thus remote from any surface connection.

Above and facing page: Pumping/winding-engine house at Guide's Shaft, Higher Bal (Higher Levant), part of the former Spearne Consols sett incorporated into Levant in 1880. The house contained a 35-in rotative, ex-stamps, engine relocated from nearby Spearne Moor Mine. Flat-rods, powered by the engine beam via the sweep-rod and crankshaft, pumped from the shaft and two winding drums were used for hoisting.

Surface archaeology here is interesting, and the shaft itself is grilled for safety. There are two arch-ways in the massive retaining wall alongside the road: one looks straight into the shaft; the second contains a flight of steep granite steps that lead up to the engine house. The V-notches in the retaining wall are ore-passes – chutes down which ore was tipped into carts that carried it to the stamps.

included the wealthy tin smelters Daubuz (Treloweth, St Erth) and Batten (Chyandour, Penzance). By 1830, the *West Briton* claimed Levant as '…for a considerable time one of

the most profitable mining concerns in the county of Cornwall'. By 1836, 320 men, 44 women and 186 children were employed, and by 1840 the mine had made a profit of

£170,000 in 20 years. It remained a predominantly rich copper producer until the 1850s and a major tin producer thereafter, until closure in 1930.

Levant used pit ponies in 1893 on the mile-long 278-fm main tramming level out under the sea – the only Cornish mine to do so in the nineteenth century (Polhigey in Wendron and East Pool & Agar in Pool did so in the twentieth century).

The name Levant echoed around the mining world when tragically, on the afternoon of 20 October 1919, the linkage between the engine and rod in Man-engine Shaft broke, sending 31 miners to their deaths. The deeper levels were never worked again, and the St Just community will never forget the fateful day when the man-engine broke.

Botallack Mine

OS Explorer 102: SW364332

Botallack Mine, just over a mile north of St Just, is one of Cornwall's most painted and photographed mines, being visited by British royalty twice: the Duke and Duchess of Cornwall (the Prince and Princess of Wales, later King Edward VII and Queen Alexandra) in 1865, and Queen Elizabeth II in 1980; the French Prince de Joinville also visited, in 1852. Allow a good couple of hours to see extensive and varied remains in a stunning setting, now in the care of the NT. A useful introduction can be found in the Counthouse (accounthouse, 1862), with limited parking

Right: 'The Crowns' engine houses of Botallack Mine, dramatically perched on Crowns Rocks, Botallack Head. The lower engine house was built in 1835 to house a 30-in Harvey's of Hayle pumping engine serving Engine Shaft; the ruined walls of its boiler houses can be seen at the rear (seaward) of the house. The higher engine house, completed in 1862, contained the all-enclosed Pearce's 24-in whim to serve the Boscawen Diagonal Shaft. The walls of its boiler house can be seen to the right of the engine house, with a steeply inclined flue (out of shot) coursing halfway up the cliff where it formerly terminated in a stack.

The principal scant remains of Crowns whim comprise this truncated granite-rubble stack, a landmark on Botallack Head. The former engine hoisted ore discharged from Boscawen Incline Shaft up a very steep skip-road cut into the cliff to cliff-top dressing floors where it also powered Cornish rolls for crushing copper ore.

In 1863, Boscawen Diagonal Shaft, named after Lord Falmouth (Botallack's mineral lord) and reaching out under the Atlantic to a distance of 800 yd from the cliffs, was the scene of a tragic accident when the gig chain broke and eight men and a boy were killed as they were precipitated down the shaft.

Botallack is an ancient group of mines formerly worked for tin, copper, arsenic and a few other, rare, minerals. One of the earliest references to copper mining in Cornwall, at the 'Cudnareeve Work in Botallack', dates back to 1587 and the Elizabethan Company of Mines Royal. Around 1590, the historian John Norden wrote of Botallack, '…a little hamlet on the coaste of Irishe sea most visited with tinners, where they lodge and feede, being nere theyre mynes.'

In the early eighteenth century, a deep adit was driven to cut the Corpus Christi Lode. By the end of the century, mines later included within Botallack, such as Wheal Cock and the Crowns, were working beneath the Atlantic. Wheal Chicken, Wheal Hen and Carnyorth and Parknoweth mines – the latter two inland and rich in tin – were added to the group.

In 1836, Steven Harvey James became the mine's famous purser, and in 1842 rich copper ore was discovered in the 85-fm level on Crowns Lode, extending out under the sea.

close by. A self-guided trail leaflet is usually available, and the SWCP passes through the property. There is a great pub in Botallack village: the Queen's Arms!

The concrete remains of Botallack's 1906 tin mill, photographed from the top of the old stamps engine stack (1860), later reused by the arsenic works. The layout of the mill downslope from right to left is clear: cast concrete loadings for the 40-head battery of Californian stamps; rectangular tables floor (centre right), which housed Buss shaking tables; Frue vanner house (centre left);

and the tin floor which contained concave and convex buddles, round frame, shaking tables and kieves. A Brunton calciner (bottom left) roasted the vanner concentrates before final concentration.

This NE view also shows the 1980s steel headframe and 1908 horizontal winder stack at Allen's Shaft (sunk 1906–14).

This was the principal copper-producing lode of the mine, but was notoriously bunchy. In 1842–5, 7,200 tons of copper ore were produced, worth £74,000, at a profit of £44,000. This bunch then failed, and it was largely tin from the inland parts of the mine that kept it going for the next 50 years, peak production being in the 1860s.

Wheal Owles,
West Wheal Owles
and Wheal Edward

OS Explorer 102: SW365325
and SW362332

The remains of Wheal Owles (*owles* = cliff), about a mile NNW of St Just, include several engine houses and their context of shafts, burrows, ore floors and ancillary structures in a glorious coastal setting.

One of the most prominent landmarks in the St Just area is the lone pumping-engine house of Wheal Owles, amid burrows on elevated ground just west of Truthwall. Built in 1857 for a 36-in engine which pumped from Engine Shaft, sunk on the NW-trending Wheal Owles Lode hosted in the granite, inland, section of the mine. Nearby are the former counthouse, smithy and stables.

It was restarted around 1810 and again in 1834 as an amalgamation of eighteenth- and nineteenth-century mines including Wheal Boys and Wheal Grouse (1837), Parknoweth (1857), Wheal Drea (1859), Wheal Edward (1863) and Cargodna (or West Wheal

View north to the 36-in pumping-engine house of West Wheal Owles (Cargodna). During the latter years of Wheal Owles, tin output was raised almost solely from this seaward section, until the notorious disaster of 1893 closed the mine.

Owles, 1870). The mine was run by the Boyns dynasty of mine managers; first John, later Richard, his nephew, who became its famous purser and manager 1855–93. The Owles group produced large quantities of black tin until the mid-1880s, when production halved due to falling ore-grades and tin prices; the workforce of 221 in 1880 reduced to 110 by 1887. Ores of copper, arsenic, bismuth and uranium are also recorded.

At just before 9 a.m. on Tuesday 10 January, 1893, miners in the 65-fm level, Cargodna, holed through to a 'House of water' in the abandoned and flooded workings of Wheal Drea. Nineteen men and a boy could not escape the torrential flood; the mine was abandoned and their bodies were never recovered. A plaque at Cargodna Shaft commemorates the tragedy.

This rotative beam-engine house is best known as Wheal Edward stamps. It drove 32 heads of Cornish stamps in the 1880s; the bluebells are growing in the remains of a 50-ft-diameter convex buddle, Cornwall's biggest and Captain Boyns' pride of the mine's tin floors. Extensive, though overgrown, remains of these floors may be found extending for 120 yd SW of the engine house.

After Wheal Owles closed, Botallack took up a lease of the mine, but the principal work involved merely a few miners doing a little prospecting above water-level for the uranium ore pitchblende (the mine is still known for its rare uranium minerals). One cask of pitchblende, showing good values for radium, was sent to Mme Curie's laboratory in France. Atomic research in the 1950s drew further attention to Wheal Edward when some pitchblende was recovered.

The prominent engine house of Wheal Drea (drea = hamlet, homestead) around 100 yd SE of Kenidjack Farm and adjacent to the remnants of the old settlement of Kenidjack. The engine house contained a 26-in rotative engine which likely wound from several shafts: possibly Greenland's Shaft some 100 yd to the NE (where some vestiges of burrows survive), and also from Wheal Drea Shaft 100 yd SSW (where a fine granite masonry collar survives amid prominent iron-rich dumps which spill down to Old Foundry Road that leads down from Nancherrow Bridge).

Cape Cornwall Mine

OS Explorer 102: SW351318

Just over a mile NW of St Just, a solitary stack of Cape Cornwall Mine crowns the 229-ft-high summit of the cape, a prominent daymark for mariners in the Western Approaches where the Atlantic currents split into the Bristol and English channels.

The ornate stack was built after 1864 to serve the Cornish boiler of a whim engine of the relatively unsuccessful Cape Cornwall tin mine. The engine was located in a tall engine house near the white-painted former mine counthouse (top right), just to the left of the track-side house which incorporates the remains of the boiler house; the engine house was demolished not long after the mine was finally abandoned in 1883. From here a long, curving stone flue connected with the stack, providing a draught which, in the event, proved too fierce. A replacement stack was built much further downslope about 1880.

Many St Just miners were also fishermen, and boats drawn up on the slipway at Porth Just (Priest's Cove) have been a feature here for generations.

The walled structures on the low cliff-top are former terraced walled gardens, built on Cape Cornwall's old tin floors, and once contained greenhouses and vineries. They were built by a St Just miner, Francis Oats, a mining engineer who rose through the ranks and later made a fortune overseas. In 1874, he was appointed the Cape Colony Government Mining and Engineering Officer in South Africa, and soon gained extensive interests in the De Beers Mine. In 1889, Cecil Rhodes gained control of Kimberley diamonds by creating one large corporate body: De Beers Consolidated Mines Ltd, with Oats as one of its directors. Oats built Porthledden House overlooking Cape Cornwall in 1907–10. The mat of dark green on the cliff-side is a carpet of mesembryanthemums, no doubt brought back the 6,000 miles from that other cape.

Cape Cornwall Mine was a relatively unremarkable tin mine, operational 1838–49 (probably its most productive phase) and 1864–9 as part of St Just Consolidated Mines, then 1870–75 independently, and finally 1879–83 as part of St Just United.

The slaty eminence of Cape Cornwall is one of only two capes in Britain.

Boswedden Mine

OS Explorer 102: SW356322

Boswedden Mine is located in the tranquil Kenidjack Valley, less than a mile NW of St Just (which has plenty of refreshments). The SWCP passes through the site and exploration, though perhaps a bit arduous, is well worth the effort. Don't miss the newly consolidated arsenic works further up the valley.

Boswedden Mine was formed in 1836 from the consolidation of several smaller

The Kenidjack Valley viewed from above the sea at Porth Ledden Cove, north of Cape Cornwall. This NE view shows the remains of Boswedden Mine and a valley packed with the industrial archaeology of water-power. You can see an impressive masonry waterwheel pit (centre, right), and leat systems (manmade watercourses) which took water from the stream and supplied Boswedden, Cape Cornwall Mine and St Just United (skirting the hillside on the right). The burrows to the right of the wheel-pit belong to Praze Shaft, which yielded copper down to 50 fm and tin below that depth. The solitary engine house of Wheal Owles at Truthwall is just discernible on the skyline.

concerns, including Wheal Call (or Caul), Wheal Castle and Great Weeth Mine. Copper and tin were mined, and five steam engines were eventually installed in the lower part of the valley, two of which operated solely during periods of prolonged dry weather. Various scant evidence of these survive, including upstanding remains of a stamps-engine house further upstream, above rectangular walled enclosures of the mine's tin floors. Operations from 1872 were included with Wheal Cunning and Boscean Mine as Wheal Cunning United, which ceased production about 1876 – truly tough times for the St Just

The massive wheel-pit of dressed granite was built about 1865 to accommodate a wheel of 52 ft diameter. It pumped from two shafts by means of flat-rods and also powered tin-dressing buddles located just to the left of the stream, the archway perpendicular to the slot of the wheel-pit serving as an outlet for shafting and bevel-gearing.

neighbourhood. In 1892, a flash flood devastated the surface remains of the mine.

In 1837, at 65-ft diameter, the famous Wheal Call Great Wheel at Boswedden in the Kenidjack Valley was one of the largest waterwheels in Britain.

Geevor Mine

OS Explorer 102: SW375345

Geevor Mine lies on the narrow coastal plain west of Penwith Moors and seaward of the B3306 at Pendeen. It is the largest preserved twentieth-century tin mine in the world, and one of the principal mining heritage sites in Cornwall.

Geevor weathered many storms until the global tin price crash of 1985: pumps were

Geevor Mine's extensive surface complex – 67 acres, including 2 acres of listed buildings – occupies a shallow, sloping, SE–NW-trending valley which meets the Atlantic at Trewellard Zawn, less than a mile SW of Pendeen lighthouse. On the left are former smallholdings created by the enclosure of commons in the nineteenth century.

finally turned off in 1991, and the site was acquired by Cornwall County Council (now Cornwall Council). Today it is a museum and a World Heritage Site visitor and educational facility, managed by members of the community its closure so recently devastated. Al-

The steel headframe (1954) of Victory Shaft is both a familiar landmark and a distinctive daymark along this rugged coastline. The sinking of Victory Shaft, named in honour of Allied victory in the Great War (1914–18), commenced in 1919. From 1974 to 1979, the Victory Shaft Sub-incline was sunk from 15 level (1,500 ft from surface) *to 19 level, extending out under the sea for ½ mile. It was officially opened by Queen Elizabeth II in 1980. There were plans to sink another sub-incline shaft into Botallack Mine, hence the clearance of Allen's Shaft and the erection of the colliery headframe which survives. Geevor reached a depth of over 2,100 ft.*

low at least four hours for your visit; perhaps combine it with the adjacent Levant.

As well as retaining a high proportion of its machinery, the site incorporates eighteenth-century underground workings, mid-nineteenth-century mine structures and a well-preserved Brunton calciner, all embedded in a tin-mill complex whose development spans

An old stables and counthouse of North Levant Mine survive.

most of the twentieth century. Victory Shaft and its associated buildings (look for the old steam winder as well as the massive modern electric one) include the evocative miners' dry and the colossal tin mill. An underground visit to a shallow level of the eighteenth-century workings of Wheal Mexico gives a good taste of conditions underground prior to the mechanization of later-twentieth-century operations. Don't miss the new Hard Rock museum, and also look out for the oldest buildings on the site – opposite the excellent café and shop – remnants of North Levant Mine which preceded Geevor.

There has been mining on the site for centuries. The name Geevor derives from the Cornish *Stennack an Gever* (goat's tin ground). North Levant & Geevor Ltd was formed in 1905, and included Wheal Carne and North Levant Mine, formed in 1851 from small ventures including Huel an Gever, Wheal Mexico, Wheal Stennack and East Levant Mine. Operations were centred on the main shaft, Wethered, next to the main road and marked today by the rebuilt wooden headgear.

Geevor Tin Mines was incorporated in 1911, employing 127 miners underground and 63 surface workers. From the 1920s, the main shaft was Victory, with the mill below being extended in the 1930s. Geevor eventually expanded its boundaries and included the Boscaswell mines, Levant and Botallack, Wheal Carne and Pendeen Consols. Geevor and South Crofty were now the largest tin producers in Cornwall. Tin prices began to soar in the 1960s, and rich ore bodies were discovered, such as Simm's and Grenfell lodes. High tin prices persisted, albeit with artificial price intervention by the International Tin Council, until the spectacular collapse of October 1985 when the price halved overnight. By the end of the year, the price had dropped from over £10,000 per tonne to under £3,000 per tonne. Wheal Concorde and Pendarves Mine closed in 1988, Geevor in 1990, Wheal Jane and Mount Wellington in 1991, and South Crofty in 1998.

Wheal Hearle
(East Boscaswell Mine)

OS Explorer 102: SW390342

Engine houses of Wheal Hearle, later known as East Boscaswell Mine, beside the B3318 Boscaswell Downs road, ½ mile ESE of Pendeen Church. On the right is a pumping-engine house that contained a 30-in engine on Borlase's Engine Shaft, which dates from the first working. The engine also drove stamps: the rear elevation, pictured,
shows architecture for a back-bob and a narrow flywheel slot to the left of the lintel-headed cylinder doorway. The engine house on the left, built in 1871, contained a whim engine which hauled from a shaft 50 ft away, with which it is aligned, and also powered stamps. The mine was operational 1853–65 (as Wheal Hearle) and again 1871–5 (as East Boscaswell), and produced mostly tin, though a little copper was mined in the earlier working.

The view looks eastwards from Carn Eanes, across the shallow higher Portheras Valley, anciently streamed for tin, with Chun Downs rising on the right and Ding Dong Mine on the skyline.

St Ives Mining District

Wheal Sisters (Trencrom Mine)

Early-summer view (NNE) to the ivy-clad pumping-engine house at Michell's Shaft of Trencrom Mine, Wheal Sisters, mid-way between Trink Hill and Trencrom Hill. Knill's Monument is on Vorvas Hill (skyline, top left). Trencrom Mine, the eastern section of Wheal Sisters, was owned by the Wheal Mary adventurers.

OS Explorer 102: SW513367

Wheal Sisters worked a group of ENE-trending tin and copper lodes for over 1½ miles between Nancledra valley in the west and Trevarrack valley in the east. 'Sisters' – principally Mary, Margaret and Kitty – was an amalgamation, in 1875, of separate mines which

View south from Trink Hill to an engine house on the Wheal Kitty/Polpeor section of the Wheal Sisters group. The mine probably has its origins in the mid-eighteenth century Providence Mine in 'Powlpear'. In the 1850s and 1860s Wheal Kitty was doing well, but temporary closure came in 1873 after which Bolitho, Harvey & Co and others took up the mine under the name of Polpeor. Ludgvan church tower and Mount's Bay are visible in the distance.

date back to the eighteenth century. In order of size they were: Wheal Mary (the oldest) held by Michell of Marazion, who also owned Trereife Tin Smelting House in Newlyn from 1861; Wheal Margaret, held by the Bolithos, who owned Chyandour Tin Smelting House in Penzance; and Wheal Kitty, also held by the Bolithos and Harvey & Co, Hayle. The mine was recapitalized in 1890, but closed finally in 1909.

Wheal Mary's tin ore was stamped at Trelocke Stamps in the Red River Valley south of Nancledra: these have been rescued, restored and are on display at Geevor Mine.

In April 1886, an engine house stack of Wheal Sisters was struck by lightning, and its top half demolished. Two miners suffered a mild electric shock – underground in the 200-fm level.

Giew Mine

OS Explorer 102: SW501372

Giew Mine, also known as South Providence, is located on the western flank of Trink Hill either side of the B3311 St Ives–Penzance road. The familiar landmark engine house, 50 yd east of the road, is at Frank's Shaft in the easternmost part of the sett. There is a convenient car-park, and less than ¼ mile away is the Engine Inn at Cripplesease.

Giew Mine has early eighteenth-century origins as a tin mine (Gehue Bounds, 1713), but during the nineteenth century it either bore other names or was part of other concerns: Wheal Gue (1819), Wheal Reeth Consols (1836–58), Billia Consols (1865–7), Giew Consols (1867–70), and Giew or South Providence (1870–78). In the twentieth century, Giew became part of St Ives Consolidated Mines Ltd (1907–15) and St Ives Mines Ltd (1915–23). With tin prices high, around £1,500 per ton, Baltrink Tin Ltd diamond-drilled Giew (1965–7), but poor results discouraged any further work.

Rear view, looking NW, of the Giew (South Providence Mine) engine house beside the B3311. It was built in 1871 for a second-hand 50-in pumping engine installed at the 244-fm Frank's Shaft in 1873. Giew, as such, worked 1870–78. Top-floor windows still contain their iron window frames, but the middle floor windows were probably infilled during the reworking as part of St Ives Consolidated Mines Ltd which commenced in 1907, after which the engine house was used as an ore bin. Giew is distinguished as the only active Cornish tin producer during the industry depression of 1921, though closure came in 1923. Remains of the boiler house stand to the left (west) of the engine house, and further up the hill can be seen a fine engine pond.

Rosewall Hill Mine

OS Explorer 102: SW496393

Two stumpy stacks on the eastern flank of Rosewall Hill, a mile SW of St Ives, are a familiar landmark to travellers entering St Ives from the west. They are remnants of Rosewall Hill Mine, the lower one serving a 36-in pumping engine on Engine Shaft, the higher one serving a 20-in whim engine. They date from about 1836, and lay immediately north of a NE–SW-trending line of shafts, openworks

and burrows: prolific evidence of eighteenth- and nineteenth-century tin mining.

Rosewall Hill Mine was an important eighteenth-century tin mine, said to have worked continually 1761–1811 to a depth of 132 fm below adit. Several small-scale reopenings and closures followed, including 1845–50. In 1857, working resumed under the name of Rosewall Hill & Ransom United, and in 1865 the mine employed 120 men, 30 boys and 20 women. Closure came in 1876, following several years of falling tin prices and rising competition from Australian output.

Tyringham Consols

St Ives Wheal Allen

OS Explorer 102: SW494386

View north to the 40-in pumping-engine house, below the Towednack Road to the south of Rosewall Hill, just over 100 yd west of Bussow Farm.

Old Bussow Mine was active in the early nineteenth century; the name Tyringham derives from the mineral lords, the Tyringham family (formerly Praed) of Trevethoe Mansion, Lelant. The mine worked for tin in the granite of Rosewall Hill around 1860 (when the engine house was erected), and was subsequently called Bussow, and Buzza, in the late 1860s. In 1880–83 it worked as West Providence Mine, no doubt referring to the rich Providence Mines of Lelant, big tin producers from the mid-1850s to mid-1870s.

OS Explorer 102: SW498400

This graceful, solitary stack is visible north of the B3306 and B3311 approaching St Ives. It lies in a field 200 yd NE of Folly Farm and, with some overgrown burrows, is all that remains of this small mine named after the Allen family of St Ives who owned it in 1730. It was reopened as Wheal Folly in 1828, but the 1862–8 working produced the greatest output: 116 tons of black tin. The engine house, formerly on the far side of the stack, was demolished in the early 1900s; the stack was preserved at the wishes of Lady Hain, wife of Sir Edward, owner of The Hain Steamship Company and the land on which Wheal Allen stood. Water from the mine augmented the supply to St Ives.

Ding Dong Mine

OS Explorer 102: SW435344

Ding Dong Mine is located on Burnt Downs, less than a mile NE of Lanyon Quoit on the road from Morvah to Madron. Public footpaths access much of the site, and make for bracing moorland walks in winter with fantastic views to Mount's Bay on a clear day. There are also several fascinating and enigmatic prehistoric monuments in the vicinity which can be combined to make a day of it.

The mine is mentioned by John Norden in about 1600, and during the eighteenth century a great number of tin bounds were active here. Some had fascinating names, no doubt later recalled in more than 20 lodes: Badger, Bosiliack, Boys, Bucka and Bussa; Jilbert's, Klucky, Providence and Qualk. Ding Dong Shaft was located in the central part of this and was the scene of a legal wrangle between Richard Trevithick, who became engineer to the mine in the 1790s, and Boulton & Watt who served an injunction due to the infringement of James Watt's condenser patent by the mine's Bull engine.

In 1813 an amalgamation of 16 separate mines created Ding Dong Mine, worked successfully by a company of adventurers

Whim-engine house; flywheel/winding drum slot to the fore. Engine house and crankshaft loading are of granite 'moorstone'; almost the entire bob-wall is roughly dressed. It housed a 25-in engine, and probably wound from several nearby shafts.

Right: View NE along the surface of 1½ mile-long x ¾ mile-wide 'swarm' of tin lodes worked latterly under the name of Ding Dong Mine. The engine house, built on top of a mine burrow of reddened hematized granite, is a familiar landmark on Penwith moors. It contained a 40-in pumping engine supplied new by Harvey's of Hayle in 1857 for use on Engine Shaft. It was relocated here, to the 80-fm Greenburrow Shaft in the old Wheal Malkin part of the sett, in 1865. The rear of the house (with adjoining stack) has no gable, there never was one: it possessed an unusual hipped roof, as did two other engine houses which survive on the mine.

who had prominent tin smelters among their ranks, notably the Bolitho family of Chyandour Smelting Works in Penzance. (Two of their stunning historic gardens near Penzance – Trengwainton and Trewidden, known for their exotic plants – are open to visitors.) Abandonment finally came in 1877 when the lodes were virtually exhausted and black tin fetched a mere £41 per ton, under half what it was five years previously. The burrows were hand-picked for ore during the early twentieth century.

100 yd north of the engine houses is the counthouse and miners' accommodation, now used as a clubhouse for Bosigran climbers. The classic Bosigran Ridge, above Porthmoina Cove, is also known as Commando Ridge.

Carn Galver Mine

OS Explorer 102: SW421364

Engine houses of Carn Galver Mine (otherwise Rosemergy Mine or Wheal Rose) stand beside the scenic B3306 St Ives–St Just road, just over a mile NE of Morvah, and ½ mile west of Carn Galver. The NT owns the engine houses and much of the land in the area, and has provided a small car-park; the SWCP here is fabulous at any time of the year.

Carn Galver worked on a reasonably extensive scale to a depth of nearly 70 fm during the 1830s. There were two steam engines on the mine and around 150 fm of continuous stopes along the strike of the lode. When the mine was reworked from 1851, an adit was commenced from the sea on a crosscourse. By 1869, 250 fm had been driven, with ventilation provided by water pressure and air piping – subsequently Mr Coulson's 'hydro-pneumatic ventilating apparatus'! The adit holed through to Engine Shaft at a depth of 70 fm from surface and drained the old flooded workings. The mine became part of Morvah and Zennor United.

Walk down the Porthmoina Valley, once streamed for tin, for about 600 yd, to where

The western engine house (left), with integral surviving stack, contained a 40-in pumping engine that served Engine Shaft. The eastern, more complete, engine house contained a 20-in winding engine.

the stream cuts down in its final run to Porthmoina Cove, and you will see the impressive remains of a water-powered tin mill at Castle Stamps.

Clear view of sea and sky through three storeys of the rear elevation of the pumping-engine house: the cylinder arch through to the cylinder plat and driver's floor, the middle chamber and bob-loft windows. The two square openings were for spring beams, a pair of longitudinal timbers either side of the beam in the top floor, also extending out under the bob-plat above the shaft at the front of the house.

Morvah Consols

OS Explorer 102: SW405359

View eastwards from the ruins of Morvah Consols to the engine house and counthouse of Garden Mine on Watch Croft.

The principal built remains of Morvah Consols overlook the steep cliff slope of Trevowhan Cliff and Zawn Alley, a short walk from the B3306, about 600 yd NE of Morvah Church. Remains of an engine house (built in 1873 and heavily damaged by American army engineers during the Second World War) stand next to Hammon's Shaft.

This formerly contained Holland's 24-in pumping and stamping engine, bought second-hand from Balleswidden, recylindered by Holman's Foundry (St Just) and at work here by 1874. Remains of a miners' dry and a walled tin floor containing two buddles lie immediately to the west. The mine's beginnings relate anciently to tin; copper was mined during the first half of the nineteenth century (certainly by 1851). The majority of built remains can be attributed to 1871–5, when a little over 5 tons of black tin was sold.

A quartz leader of Zawn Alley Lode can be plainly seen in a large rock at the base of the cliffs.

Trevega Bal

OS Explorer 102: SW482405

Clearly visible from the B3306 skirting Rosewall Hill is the remains of the stamps-engine house of Trevega Bal, ½ mile north of Trevega. Its ruined state is partly due to a German plane jettisoning a bomb in the Second World War.

Trevega comprised a group of eighteenth-century mines including Wheal Brea and Wheal Fat which worked dozens of small, sometimes rich, parallel tin lodes. Trevigha Bal (later Trevega) is reputedly the first mine in Penwith where gunpowder blasting was introduced, by two 'eastern' men – Bell and Care – about 1700. In the 1860s it was also known as Brea Consols, Trevessa & Brea Mines, and then West St Ives Consols. Three adits penetrate the cliffs at Brea Cove, and good crosscourse sulphide mineralization may be seen there at low tide.

Garden Mine (Morvah Hill Mine)

OS Explorer 102: SW417357

The bob-wall of the ruined pumping-engine house of Garden Mine forms a landmark on a clear day, 370 yd west of the summit of Watch Croft. At an elevation of over 700 ft above sea level, it is at the highest elevation of any mine in west Cornwall. Garden Mine included a number of ancient tin workings, and became part of Morvah and Zennor United which, in 1838, employed 116 people.

Godolphin Mining District

Wheal Vor

OS Explorer 103: SW625303

The scattered and relatively scant remains of Wheal Vor lay around 2 miles NW of Helston and a mile north of Breage. 'Relatively' because, during the first half of the nineteenth century, this was Cornwall's richest and greatest tin mine, covering some 1,400 acres of ground at surface and, in 1836, giving employment to 592 men, 327 women and 255 children. Though much has long been swept away, there are a few interesting monuments set in a landscape that is reverting to rural farmland and smallholdings.

Wheal Vor (Great Mine) was an ancient working for tin, and copper, in killas, whose beginnings may possibly go back to opencast workings in the Romano-British period. Mining was certainly taking place during the fifteenth century, probably in association with the Godolphin family. At the beginning of the eighteenth century, Wheal Vor was a pioneer of steam power. The first metal mine in the world to do so, it is thought to have hosted Savery trials in 1698, and installed Cornwall's first Newcomen engine (some say the first ever Newcomen engine on a mine) between 1710 and 1716. In 1816–17, some of the first steam-powered stamps were installed at Wheal Vor, and later, in 1854, the largest steam-pumping engine on any mine in the world was erected on Crease's Shaft (formerly Borlase's) – the Harvey's of Hayle 100-in. Harvey's were major shareholders in a new company which began draining the old mine's 30 miles of workings in 1853 and reworking the mile-long ENE–WSW Main Lode for tin; unfortunately this heralded the greatest single financial loss in the history of Cornish mining – over £200,000 by 1860. Wheal Vor's heyday was during the period of reworking, 1812–48, by a company formed in 1810 by John Gundry who, with three brothers, were bankers and merchants of Goldsithney. The mine cut it rich in 1823, and in 1824–33, Wheal Vor Consolidated mined and smelted around 10,000 tons of metal – over 20 per cent of total Cornish output at the time. Messrs Gundry, however,

Pumping-engine house at Ivey's Shaft, Wheal Metal section, Great Wheal Vor United. The fine engine house contained a Harvey & Co 85-in engine moved from Trelawny's Shaft in the main part of the Wheal Vor sett when it was abandoned in 1860. Together with the principal masonry of its former engine house, it was erected at 90° to an existing 60-in pumping engine on Ivey's Shaft; the change-over to the more powerful engine, using the same pitwork, remarkably took only three days. In 1863, Ivey's Shaft was being deepened through ore-ground worth an amazing £300–£500 per fm, with £70,000 of tin ore laid open in less than a year. In 1868,
a man-engine was installed to 120 fm, powered by a 30-in Bull engine. Wheal Metal worked parallel tin lodes south of those of Great Wheal Vor, and gave excellent profits during the latter working; profits, however, which were swallowed up in the ocean of loss incurred by the old mine. The Mining & Smelting Magazine commented, 'Altogether the courses of tin met with in Wheal Metal exceed in richness any recently found in Cornwall; if this mine all through had been worked vigorously, and independently of old Wheal Vor, it would have been distinguished as one of the great modern successes of Cornish mining.'

had run into financial difficulties long before Wheal Vor's startling success, and the brothers were declared bankrupts in 1819. Their

failure subsequently led to great litigation, which continued to the immense profit of lawyers who pocketed hundreds of thou-

The 30-in rotative stamping/pumping-engine house at Watson's Shaft, Wheal Metal & Flow, its boiler house being linked to the ornate stack by a buried flue. The sett of the Flow was added to Great Wheal Vor United in 1853, but Wheal Metal & Flow commenced operations in 1885 when this engine was installed to work the Wheal Vor burrows and tailings. Watson's Shaft of the old West Wheal Metal was used as a water supply, the engine having a 'back-bob', to supply the tin mill which operated from 1885 to 1906, and produced just over 600 tons of black tin.

Stack at Wheal Metal & Flow on the western flank of Carnmeal Downs, south of Wheal Vor. The stack served the boilers of a stamps engine 30 yd to the NW, and is unusually ornate in its detail: diamond-patterned white and red brickwork, and even a black band of tourmalinized bedded killas in the predominantly granite rubble course.

sands of pounds during a period of 32 years. A vigorous attempt to rework Wheal Vor took place at the beginning of the twentieth century. Overall, Wheal Vor is estimated to have produced more than 60,000 tons of black tin.

A solitary engine house of Polladras (or Polladrass) Downs Mine, ½ mile north of Carleen. Polladras was an ancient mine, certainly active from the early-eighteenth century. John Gundry of Goldsithney owned almost half of the mine when, in 1810, a 24-in steam engine was installed. It closed again in 1816, but subsequently became part of Wheal Vor Consolidated, later Great Wheal Vor United.

Great Work Mine

OS Explorer 102: SW596308

Great Work is situated in the saddle of Godolphin and Tregonning hills, just under a mile SW of Godolphin Cross and roughly 4 miles west of Helston. The engine house and telescoped stack at Leeds Shaft are owned by the NT, acquired as part of the 550-acre Godolphin Estate in 2000. There is a small car-park at Great Work but at Godolphin House, bought by the NT in 2007 and now being restored, is a car-park from where the Estate walks start. The climb to the summit of Godolphin Hill is less than a mile and provides breathtaking views of west Cornwall; from there it's a ½-mile SE descent to Great Work. When the House and Gardens are open, it's a great place for tea and cakes (and to check out progress in restoration); the Godolphin Arms is close, at Godolphin Cross.

Great Work was one of Cornwall's richest medieval tin mines, and one of the longest-lived, albeit intermittently: Leland commented around 1538 that 'There are no greater Tynne workes yn al Cornwal than be on Sir Wylliam Godolcan's Ground'. It was still a major producer in the nineteenth century, reworking again in the 1930s, with some free-setting tributers continuing until 1949. The mine contributed considerably to the rise of the Godolphin family: Sidney Godolphin (1645–1712) was a leading British politician and financial wizard of the late-seventeenth and early-eighteenth centuries, under four sovereigns. In 1684 he became Baron Godolphin and First Lord of the Treasury, and under King James II was one of his close advisers. In 1704, he was knighted, and in 1706 became the first Earl of Godolphin. Francis Godolphin (1678–1766), Sidney's only son and the second Earl, continued the family tradition at the forefront of Cornish mining technology. Their mines such as Great Work and Wheal Vor were the first in Cornwall to introduce gunpowder for blasting and the first metal mines to employ steam pumping. Francis was also the owner of the Godolphin Arabian, one of three stallions that were the founders of all modern Thoroughbred race horses. The last Godolphin of Godolphin

Right: The NT have carried out conservation and safety works around Leeds Shaft, and have provided a small car-park and circular path that takes in the principal features: pumping-engine house and stack at Leeds Shaft (grilled for safety, and for bats!), and the Cornish-hedged Burnt Whim Shaft (centre right).

The pumping-engine house and telescoped stack at Leeds Shaft served a Harvey's of Hayle 60-in pumping engine made in 1829 and recylindered in 1857. Great Work possessed a distinguished succession of Cornish engines, commencing with a 63-in Newcomen engine installed in the eighteenth century. During a reworking from 1934, the gable of the engine house was removed and a flat corrugated iron roof installed.

was William, Marquess of Blandford (1700–31), after whose death the title and property passed to Thomas Osborne (1713–89), the fourth Duke of Leeds. Leeds Shaft, and nearby Leedstown, is named after the family.

The mine worked principally for tin (though a little copper was also produced) in SW–NE-trending lodes in the Godolphin-Tregonning granite, overlain with shallow killas.

Wheal Prosper

OS Explorer 102: SW594270

Wheal Prosper worked copper and tin lodes in the southern lobe of the Godolphin-Tregonning granite mass and adjacent killas. It operated 1832–49, producing mostly copper ore, and again 1860–66 when it produced 7 tons of black tin. It was in the latter working that the surviving, 30-in pumping-engine house was built (1860); though the mine was renowned for being 'dry' in spite of its close proximity to the sea. The engine house was conserved by the NT following acquisition in 1969.

The engine house and burrows at Engine Shaft, Wheal Prosper, lay part-way down Rinsey East Cliff overlooking Porthcew Beach, just over a mile south of the A394 near Ashton and about 450 yd east of the cliff top at

Rinsey Head. The NT owns the cliffs from the eastern end of Praa Sands to the eastern end of Trewavas Cliff, and has provided a car-park where the public road ends just seaward of Rinsey and within a 250-yd walk of the engine house. Wheal Prosper may be conveniently combined with nearby Wheal Trewavas, less than ½ mile to the SE along a spectacular stretch of SWCP with views to Porthleven and the Lizard.

The pumping-engine house on the eastern side of Trewavas Head dates from 1836. In front (left) can be seen Engine (later Old Engine) Shaft which has two collars side by side, one for pumping and one for hoisting. The shaft was sunk on the Old Lode which ran out under the sea-bed in a SE direction. The unusually tall and narrow rectangular slot in the rear of the engine house was to allow the beam to be brought into the house; there is little room for manoeuvre on the seaward side! Clearly visible in the top of the curved retaining wall of the former manual capstan platform (centre right) can be seen the drum pit and rope trench pointing towards the shaft.

Wheal Trewavas

OS Explorer 102: SW597265

Substantial remains of Wheal Trewavas lie seaward of the SWCP at Trewavas Head on the southern margin of the Godolphin and Tregonning granite, 3 miles west of Porthleven. The site was acquired (and the engine houses conserved) by the NT in 2008–09. There is a NT car-park at nearby Rinsey, from which the ½-mile walk to Trewavas passes Wheal Prosper. The Lion & Lamb Inn, opposite Rinsey Lane turning off the A394 at Ashton, can help to round off a good half-day at one of Cornwall's most dramatic mine sites.

Wheal Trewavas followed SE-trending copper lodes which bunched richly beneath the sea. The mine worked for 12 years (1834–46) but proved to be rich, employing up to 200 people, and bringing a steady stream of small profits to the adventurers.

Above: Engine house and stack at New Engine Shaft, Wheal Trewavas, built in 1836 into the weathered granite cliff-slope for a Harvey's of Hayle 45-in engine. View looking SE across rough seas to Porthleven and the Lizard peninsula.

Left: Wheal Trewavas, looking north from Mount's Bay across the cliff-side engine houses and farmland to the granite hills of Tregonning and Godolphin. Site of dressing floors and burrows (out of shot, left), engine house on Old Engine Shaft (centre left), and engine house on New Engine Shaft (centre right). Wheal Trewavas was said to be 'first discovered from the sea by some of those amphibious creatures who obtain their livelihood by fishing in the summer and mining in the winter, who observed from their boats the lodes or mineral veins in the cliffs of this estate…' (Mining Journal, 17 October 1835)

Tregurtha Downs Mine

OS Explorer 102: SW537311

The engine house and stack of Tregurtha Downs Mine, ½ mile NW of the B3280 at Goldsithney, just over a mile east of Marazion. The striking architecture of distinctive slit windows and massive cylinder arch, and exceptional preservation make this an unusual engine-house conversion, complete with reconstructed bob-plat.

The story of the engine formerly housed here at Engine Shaft illustrates the not untypical mobility of Cornish beam engines: the 80-in pumping engine was built in 1854 by Copperhouse Foundry, Hayle for Alfred Consols copper mine near Hayle, where it was christened Davey's Engine. When that mine closed in 1864, it was sold to Crenver & Wheal Abraham United, a formerly rich copper mine near Leedstown, where it was known as Pelly's Engine; after that closed, it went to the Owen Vean & Tregurtha Downs Mines in 1881, the bob being raised in place at Christmas 1882 to the sound of carols, and being christened St Aubyn's Engine in 1883. Harvey & Co of Hayle bought the mine two years later; in 1889 the engine house was gutted by fire; remarkably, the engine was swiftly back to work, though mining was intermittent until closure in 1902. The engine was then bought by South Crofty Mine for the new Robinson's Shaft, where it worked for over 50 years – the last Cornish engine to work on a Cornish mine. It is now (2011) preserved in Robinson's Shaft engine house, and is due to be restored – possibly to steaming order.

Wheal Grey

West Godolphin Mine

OS Explorer 102: SW595291

The engine house, boiler house and stack of Wheal Grey, just north of the A394 near Tresowes Green, less than a mile east of Germoe Cross Roads. Tin was worked on the Tresowes Moor during the eighteenth century, and there were five tin lodes subsequently worked in heavily kaolinized and tourmalinized granite to a depth of 65 fm below adit. Wheal Grey was active in 1810, and employed 130 in 1836 but was sold in 1848, having two pumping engines, a stamps engine and ten horse whims. Wheal Grey worked in conjunction with Great Work 1868–73.

OS Explorer 102: SW585316

A conspicuous pumping-engine house of West Godolphin Mine stands on the western flank of Godolphin Hill overlooking Trescowe Common and the valley of the River Hayle (where two stacks mark the site of the mine's stamps), about 1½ miles north of Germoe. It was built in 1877 using granite masonry purchased from nearby Bosence Mine engine house on the other side of the River Hayle. Known as North Great Work Mine 1860–62 and West Godolphin 1870–90, the mine produced 1,520 tons of black tin and 214 tons of 17 per cent copper ore from the Godolphin-Tregonning granite, overlain by killas to the north. The comparatively high grade of copper ore is due to the rich mineralogy of chalcocite, tenorite and malachite. One of the lodes – the Great Junket Caunter – gives it the local name of Wheal Junket (junket = dessert of milk curdled by rennet, in Cornwall served with clotted cream).

Nancegollan Mine

OS Explorer 103: SW640323

The pumping-engine house and separate stack at Old Engine Shaft of Nancegollan Mine stand in a field close to the former station of the abandoned Helston Railway, immediately east of Nancegollan Methodist Chapel and the B3303, 3 miles NW of Helston. Nancegollan (Nans golans = small valley) was a small tin mine that worked in the vicinity of the granite-killas contact from the 1830s and reopened 1851–70, returning 6 tons of black tin in 1854.

Polcrebo Downs Mine

OS Explorer 103: SW647332

A solitary stack at Engine Shaft, Polcrebo Downs Mine, just under a mile NE of Nancegollan. Though the adjacent bob-wall ruin collapsed in a gale in 1961, the stack still forms a landmark east of the B3303 Camborne-Helston road. The mine worked for tin in granite and an elvan dyke 1860–65 and 1870–90.

Wendron Mining District

Trumpet Consols

OS Explorer 103: SW675303

Two engine houses survive out of about 12 that originally served the Trumpet group. That in the foreground is the Wheal Trumpet 30-in whim; in the distance is the 48-in pumping-engine house of Wheal Ann, connected at depth westward. Peak production of the group exceeded 2,300 tons of black tin in the decade 1864–73, after which, with tin prices falling and the cost of coal increasing, the mine disappeared from the dividend list: shares fell from £17 to £3 in two years, and the mine closed in 1877. A reworking as New Trumpet Consols (1881–8) returned a little over 500 tons of copper ore and around 14 tons of black tin.

Wheal Trumpet whim. Old Wheal Trumpet was active from 1810, and was exceedingly rich in the 1820s when its principal shareholder was Thomas Teague, manager of Tresavean Mine near Lanner; the Duchy was mineral lord. Wheal Trumpet worked six lodes, mostly for tin, and closed in 1832. It became the largest section of the Trumpet Consols group when working resumed in 1850. Little remains today as context for this engine house, except a few plugged shafts and the walls of a former yard or building 130 yd WSW.

These two engine houses are landmarks on the B3297 Redruth–Helston road, ½ mile SW of Wendron. This group of mines was among the deepest and richest in the Wendron Mining District, working ENE–WSW-trending tin lodes (with some copper) in the granite-killas contact zone near the southern margin of the Carnmenellis granite mass.

The old and unusual house of Wheal Ann on the east part of the Trumpet group. The corbelled bob-wall (with no plug doorway) supported a wooden bob of a 48-in pumping engine. Wheal Ann closed on the death of its principal share-holder, Thomas Teague (who owned almost half of the mine), in 1844, and the engine remained unsold until it was moved to another part of the mine (Wheal Valls) in 1850, where it continued working until 1877, being finally dismantled in 1889. The ruined stack is the result of a lightning strike some years ago.

Basset & Grylls Mine

OS Explorer 103: SW693328

The remains of Basset & Grylls Mine, for-merly Porkellis United, principally comprise an engine house and fairly extensive remains of twentieth-century workings. The latter lie

Basset & Grylls Mine pumping-engine house, standing in a small patch of woodland beside a 90° bend in the road midway between Porkellis village and Porkellis Moor. The house was built in 1859–60 at Tyacke's Shaft, named after the mine purser Joseph Tyacke of Helston, and for-merly contained a 60-in pumping engine moved from the abandoned section of the mine. It has been conserved by the NT, acquired as part of the Penrose Estate.

on, and adjoin, the easternmost segment of Porkellis Moor at Lower Porkellis, fairly close to the road. A public footpath skirts and over-looks the eastern part of the Moor, with its prolific hummocks and hollows of old-time tin-streamers, ending up at Porkellis Bridge not far from Wheal Enys. There is also an earlier engine house at Tyacke's Shaft next to the road further towards Porkellis village.

Basset & Grylls Mine was formed in 1858, taking its name from the principal mineral lord, GL Basset of Tehidy, and mine secretary and purser, Colonel Grylls (Lord Robartes of Lanhydrock also received dues). The mine succeeded the loss-making and unfortunate Porkellis United Mine that was restarted in the mid-nineteenth century to work the tin lodes discovered by tin-streamers on the desolate Porkellis Moor: in 1853 three miners were killed and two seriously injured in notoriously unstable workings in 'pot' granite, and in 1858 an extensive slimes pit collapsed into near-surface workings, entombing seven miners and closing the mine. Under Basset and Grylls, reopening part of Porkellis United and further development of up to 14 lodes returned over 2,800 tons of black tin in its peak years, 1861–74. Substantial underground operations ceased in 1875, after which output dropped considerably, though the mine limped on into the twentieth century when various reworkings resumed under the names of Rayfield Tin Syndicate, Jantar and Porkellis Tin Mines.

East Wheal Lovell

OS Explorer 103: SW699314

The 50-in pumping engine at Rogers' Shaft (after purser Henry Rogers of Helston) on the Tregonbris section of the mine is said to be the last beam engine to work in the Wendron Mining District, ceasing in 1881. East Wheal Lovell began working in 1857, taking the sett of the formerly unsuccessful Tregonbris, Carnebone & Fatwork United Mines (1853–6). Two years later, 116 men, 47 boys and 23 females were employed, and 16 tin lodes were developed from four principal shafts in granite country. The mine was notoriously bunchy: in 1869, the Cornish adventurers gave the miners a week's wages as a bonus on the discovery of a rich, 6-ft wide tin lode. In 1870, in nine months' working, £17,000-worth of tin ore was raised at a profit of nearly £13,000. Share values doubled, and over-doubled again, in under a year.

This landmark engine house, just west of the A394 Helston–Falmouth road at Carnebone, is a little over 3 miles NE of Helston.

Wheal Enys

OS Explorer 103: SW689336

The 24-in stamps-engine house of Wheal Enys, converted into a dwelling, 1/4 mile NW of Porkellis village. The Copperhouse Foundry (Sandys Vivian) engine, installed in 1852, was offered for sale in 1860 with 32 heads of stamps after producing a little over 250 tons of black tin. The façade of Porkellis Wesleyan Chapel sourced dressed granite from the demolition of the pumping-engine house in 1866. John Samuel Enys (1796–1872) of Enys, Penryn, was mineral lord.

Medlyn Moor Mine

OS Explorer 103: SW706335

The engine house of Medlyn Moor Mine is about 2½ miles NE of Wendron in the shallow, marshy valley that runs for ½ mile south

The 1870s 40-in pumping-engine house. Engine Shaft was vertical, working three lodes from levels at 17, 27 and 33 fm below surface. Water-filled shafts (one, traditionally hedged, right of the engine house), swampy hollows among willow and shrubby blackthorn, and gorse-covered remnants of burrows are further reminders of industry.

from Medlyn Farm to join the River Cober. Old tin-streamers' workings are now a haven for wildlife, and a footpath accesses Medlyn Moor from the Porkellis–Carnkie road.

Tin-streamers discovered the lodes in deeply weathered granite beneath the alluvials. They worked them by openworks, then by shallow mining as Wheal Medlyn in the early 1850s, on a lease from mineral lord Sir Charles Lemon (1784–1868), using a 23-in engine and 21-ft waterwheel. Finally, the Medlyn Moor Mining Company employed over 20 miners underground, returning some 80 tons of black tin in 1873–80.

Camborne-Redruth Mining District

Dolcoath Mine

OS Explorer 104: SW660403

New East Shaft whim-engine house and boiler house looking ENE to Carn Brea. Its unusual appearance (filling in above the bob-wall and a new arched window) is due to its conversion into an electricity sub-station.

The remains of this ancient and once mighty mine, that produced both copper and tin in enormous quantities, lie less than a mile east of Camborne. A number of buildings survive, though somewhat distant from each other

Harriett's Shaft engine house looking SE to the site of Williams Shaft (named after Dolcoath Chairman Michael Williams) on Carn Entral. The engine house, on one of Dolcoath's principal shafts, was built in 1860 to house a Perran Foundry 60-in pumping engine, later recylindered to 65 in. Together with a former carpenter's workshop, it stands immediately overlooking the mainline railway, just to the west of the level crossing at Lower Pengegon. An impressive miners' dry is behind the camera.

Dolcoath incorporated several adjacent mines, including Stray Park in 1871. This 65-in pumping-engine house at Stray Park Engine Shaft, photographed during conservation work, stands along a residential street backed by the railway.

and with little context left considering the size of the operation. They include three readily encountered engine houses, a compressor house, counthouse, miners' dry, and Williams

Shaft winder house on the NW flank of Carn Entral. Most buildings have been conserved and shafts capped, with a series of paths created in order to explore the sites.

Dolcoath, like a number of other mines in the Central Mining District, was a rich copper producer during the eighteenth century (the name Dolcoath appearing in 1738), and a prolific tin producer in the later-nineteenth century, finally closing in 1921. Recorded production includes over 350,000 tons of copper ore (ranking fifth in Cornwall) and around 100,000 tons of black tin (first in Cornwall), which places Dolcoath as a true champion of Cornish mines. It also did rather well for mineral lords the Bassets of Tehidy, who received royalties from nearly £10 million-worth of mineral sales.

By 1758, Dolcoath was already rich enough to possess a Newcomen engine, installed by engineer Richard Trevithick Senior, although closure came 1788–99, due to market pressures rather than lack of ore. During the nineteenth century, Dolcoath became the deepest mine in Cornwall, a status that remained unchanged, its eventual depth being over 3,000 ft. In the 1840s, copper production tailed off, but from the 1850s rich tin was raised from greater depths under the direction of Captain Charles Thomas; arsenic, tungsten, silver, lead, cobalt, bismuth and uranium were also produced. The deeper Dolcoath mined, the richer it became: in 1886 the mine was well over 2,000 ft deep and Main Lode was 18 ft wide. In 1893, there was a major collapse at the famous 412-fm level (nearly ½ mile down), when a 'forest' of 18-in square x 33-ft long pitch-pine timbers gave way, killing seven miners. In 1895, shaft-sinking commenced at the vertical Williams Shaft on Carn Entral. At over 3,000 ft, it came into use in 1911.

Dolcoath closed in 1921, was unsuccessfully reopened by sinking the new Roskear Shaft, and was acquired by South Crofty Mine in 1936, forming what eventually became a very productive addition to Cornwall's last tin mine of the twentieth century.

East Pool & Agar Mine

OS Explorer 104: SW675418

The site of East Pool & Agar Mine, and of the earlier East Pool Mine, lay north and south of the A3047 at Pool, between Camborne and Redruth. There are two engine houses, both remarkably containing their original beam engines, cared for by the NT and open to the public (see Cornish Mines & Engines for opening times). Mitchell's Shaft Whim (North Whim, also known as Michell's Whim after the engineer) is right beside the road; the Taylor's Shaft complex of East Pool & Agar is 350 yd NNE, accessed from the far end of the supermarket car-park. There are interpretive displays at each site, and excellent guides on hand to answer questions; a must to visit.

East Pool Mine was one of Cornwall's rich and successful mines. As Pool Adit, in the eighteenth century, it made a fortune out of copper for the Bassets of Tehidy. It reopened in 1834 and, like other mines in the Central Mining District, changed output from copper (after producing over 90,000 tons of ore) to tin (producing nearly 50,000 tons of black tin) as it approached the contact at depth with the Carn Brea granite. East Pool was also one of Cornwall's largest producers of tungsten and arsenic in its later years, and produced small amounts of cobalt and bismuth. In 1897, East Pool was amalgamated with its neighbour Wheal Agar to become

Right: Aerial view looking north to the Taylor's Shaft complex, East Pool & Agar Mine, built in the 1920s. The massive 90-in pumping engine with 52-ton bob can be seen in its house (higher centre), with roofless boiler house to the right and stack – over 100 ft high – bearing the initials EPAL (the stack served boiler houses for both the pump and winder). The winder house can be seen at the top of the 'T' formed with the larger compressor house at 90° (centre right). The winder boiler house adjoins to the right of the winder house; the capstan house adjoins to the left. The miners' dry (higher left) remains in use as a warehouse; the former mine office survives (far left) together with concrete bases of the primary crusher (centre left), and ore-loading stations for a tramway and subsequent aerial ropeway.

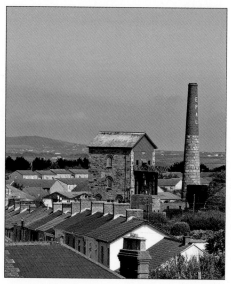

The graceful whim-engine house at Mitchell's Shaft, East Pool Mine, beside the old A30 (now A3047) at Pool. It still houses a 30-in beam winding engine, made in 1887 at Holman's Foundry, Camborne. You can just see the nose of the bob above the lattice-railed bob-plat with sweep-rod connecting to the crank and flywheel/winding drum. It was saved from being scrapped in 1941 by the Cornish Engines Preservation Society, taken into the care of the NT in 1967, and set into motion by electricity in 1975. A look at this in-situ engine helps to explain a lot of the archaeology that you might encounter when visiting less well-preserved whim-engine houses!

Taylor's Shaft engine house, St Agnes Beacon in the distance and a terrace of miners' cottages diverging away from the camera. Lord Agar-Robartes of Lanhydrock was mineral lord and landowner of Wheal Agar, and built this terrace of miners' cottages on the east side of Trevithick Road.

East Pool & Agar Mine. From the 1860s, ore was taken to the mill in the Tolvaddon Valley a mile to the west. From 1903, this was by electric tramway (part of the Camborne and Redruth Tramway), superseded in 1934 by an aerial ropeway. In 1921, a major collapse underground forced the closure of the old mine and the development, from 1922, of the new Taylor's Shaft (named after the mine manager) to the north. The 90-in pumping engine, designed by Nicholas Trestrail and built by Harvey's of Hayle in 1892, came from Carn Brea Mine where it had lain idle since 1914. In 1945 the mine closed, but Taylor's Shaft engine continued pumping the workings, which connected with those of South Crofty Mine whose sett bounded East Pool to the west, until 1954. It was subsequently saved by an American benefactor who bought it and donated it to the Cornish Engines Preservation Society. It is also interesting to note that East Pool was one of three Cornish mines that used 'pit ponies' underground, to haul ore to Taylor's Shaft.

Chappel's Shaft 26-in whim, Cook's Kitchen.

Cook's Kitchen Mine

OS Explorer 104: SW665407

Two engine houses of Cook's Kitchen Mine stand 60 yd north of the mainline railway near Brea. They are adjacent to South Crofty Mine's surface works and overlook the Red River Valley which formed along the weakness of the Great Crosscourse, separating Cook's Kitchen to the east from Dolcoath to the west. The site can be conveniently approached via a footbridge at the end of a lane leading from the Brea Inn, the engine houses being highly visible from above Brea and from passing trains.

Cook's Kitchen Mine was so named because a miner named Cook discovered a copper lode that was as wide as his kitchen (the lodes here are up to 30 ft wide). Mining on the site dates to 1744, at least. The

The pair of engine houses at Cook's Kitchen Mine served Chappel's Shaft (vertical to 60 fm below adit – 30 fm – where Chappel's Lode enters granite and then on the southerly underlie of the lode to the 430-fm level). Rich copper – famously including the rich ore chalcocite, dubbed 'Redruthite' at the time – occurred down to the 160-fm level, and tin below, being at its richest between the 200- and 400-fm levels. The larger pumping-engine house, with separate shortened stack, contained a 50-in engine in 1838 (recylindered to 55-in in 1872), and the whim a 26-in engine dating from about 1860.

railway line roughly traces the surface contact of the Carn Brea granite (dipping at 35°N) with the overlying killas to the north. Cook's Kitchen, like other large copper producers in Illogan parish, including Dolcoath, East Pool, Carn Brea and Tincroft, increasingly turned towards dominant tin production during the second half of the nineteenth century as workings left the killas and approached or entered granite. In 1850, though the *Mining Journal* commented, 'This is one of the oldest mines in Cornwall, worked formerly 200 fm deep, and yielding £200,000 profit', Cook's Kitchen had not paid a dividend since 1809, and the mine's wealth related to rich and shallow copper mined mostly during the eighteenth century.

Cook's Kitchen is famously cited in Pryce's *Mineralogia Cornubiensis* (1778) for its underground pumping waterwheels, and even in 1859–60 when a man-engine was installed to 190 fm, it was powered by a 52-ft-diameter former pumping waterwheel situated underground. The mine's next dividends came in 1861 and 1862, having begun to increasingly produce tin, but in 1872–4, shares dropped from £48 to £4 during the Australian tin crisis. At this time, the sett was divided into two: New Cook's Kitchen in the north, and Old Cook's Kitchen in the south. After struggling along, amalgamation with Tincroft Mine took place in 1895 (the two later amalgamated into the larger Carn Brea and Tincroft Mines), and in 1899 South Crofty Mine purchased New Cook's Kitchen sett.

South Crofty Mine

OS Explorer 104: SW663409

The principal remains of South Crofty Mine, situated around a mile NE of Camborne, straddle Dudnance Lane, the continuance of Tolvaddon Road that leads SE from the A30. The area around Robinson's Shaft is part of the current (2011) Heartlands regeneration project; the area around New Cook's is also likely to be redeveloped. Mining may resume if the price of tin stays high, and surface operations will probably shift to the Tuckingmill Decline area on the western side of the Red River Valley near the railway embankment.

Overleaf: View SW to New Cook's Kitchen Shaft (centre left), South Crofty Mine. The tall steel headframe, erected in 1969 on the shaft which was sunk in 1907, comprises two units, each with its own winding cables: the further, taller, one with the backlegs at an angle of around 60° on the left was used for materials and men; the nearer one, with backlegs to the right, was for hoisting ore in skips. Once ore reached the surface it was transferred on to the conveyor which fed the three tall cylindrical ore-bins. From there the ore passed into the mill for reduction and concentration, although South Crofty ore was latterly taken by lorry to the mill at Wheal Jane (closed 1991) for processing.

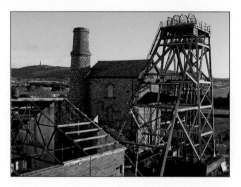

Robinson's Shaft engine house and headframe, South Crofty Mine, looking ESE to Carn Brea. This view, taken from a cherry-picker at the commencement of the Heartlands regeneration project, clearly shows the nose of the Robinson's engine beam extending out over the shaft. This much-travelled engine was an 80-in pumping engine built in 1854 by Sandys, Vivian & Co (Copperhouse Foundry) for Alfred Consols near Hayle. It was working there by 1855 (known as Davey's Engine); then moved in 1865 to Crenver and Wheal Abraham in Crowan (as Pelly's Engine), then to Tregurtha Downs near Marazion where it began work in 1883 (as St Aubyn's Engine), where it survived a disastrous engine-house fire in 1889; its house survives. Finally, it was purchased by South Wheal Crofty where it was erected at Robinson's Shaft by engineer Nicholas Trestrail in 1903. It was the last engine to work on a Cornish mine, finally stopping, after almost continuous operation at Crofty, when replaced by electric pumps in 1955. The roofless building in the left foreground is the electric-winder house.

Visitor access to Robinson's engine and to South Crofty Mine should be possible in the near future.

South Crofty is now one of Cornwall's best-known mines due to its high-profile fight for survival following the 1985 international tin crisis when prices fell from around £10,000 per tonne to around £3,300 per tonne, overnight. Final – or hopefully temporary – closure came in March 1998, but interest and activity have continued ever since.

The mineralized area later worked by South Crofty has an ancient mining history, with ventures such as Penhellick Vean and Tyn Croft recorded working in the 1680s. In 1854, the former sett of East Wheal Crofty was sub-divided into South Wheal Crofty and North Wheal Crofty. South Wheal Crofty became South Crofty Ltd in 1906.

The area is interesting from a combined historical, geographical and geological viewpoint in that mining started for shallow tin, and switched to copper and then tin at greater depths in the 1860s. Evidence on the ground shows a chronology of the mine's shifting centre of operations from NE to SW along the trend of the lodes: the 1860s phase of shafts (Palmer's and Bickford's) with remains of pumping- and winding-engine houses, boiler houses, engine pond and miners' dry next to Station Road; the 1900s phase centred on Robinson's Shaft, and the last centre of operations around New Cook's Shaft. Acquisitions in the late-nineteenth and early twentieth centuries made South Crofty a massive, interconnected sett which stretched over 2 miles – from Tolskithy Valley to Camborne – along the north of the granite ridge traced by Carn Brea, Carnarthen and Carn Entral. It included some of the richest copper producers of the eighteenth and early nineteenth centuries, and the richest tin producers of the nineteenth and early twentieth centuries: New Cook's Kitchen (the northern part of Cook's Kitchen Mine, 1893), Carn Brea & Tincroft (which also included Cook's Kitchen), Dolcoath and the Roskears (1936), and East Pool (1947).

The massive, slit-windowed, pumping-engine house at Pascoe's Shaft, South Wheal Frances. The mine was named after the Rt. Hon Frances Baroness Basset, only child of Francis Basset (1757–1835) first Lord de Dunstanville; the shaft after manager and shareholder Captain Pascoe. It housed an 80-in engine, the largest ever built by St Austell Foundry, in 1881, for Old Shepherd's Mine, St Newlyn East. It was bought for South Wheal Frances in 1887, erected by engineer Nicholas Trestrail, and started in 1888. South Frances was a notoriously wet mine: in 1879, when the old part of the Wheal Basset sett was stopped, the first cast-iron underground dam in Cornwall was installed to prevent flooding from that mine. The stoppage affected West Basset and West Wheal Frances, and the old Wheal Basset engine was kept working. Even in 1885 water-skips were used to supplement pumping. Evidence for the boiler house (this side) for four Cornish boilers is now little more than lines of flashing on the wing wall and stack, and rubble hidden among the scrub (lower right).

Basset Mines, South Wheal Frances section

OS Explorer 104: SW681394

This is one of Cornwall's most substantial, and more unusual, groups of mining remains:

the Marriott's Shaft complex built for Basset Mines Ltd, formed in 1896 to exploit tin from the Great Flat Lode. They form a striking and remarkably intact survival, some buildings almost assuming cathedral-like proportions, set in open countryside around 2 miles SW of Redruth. This is also a great location from which to access other mining remains in this central zone of the Great Flat Lode: buildings have been consolidated, shafts made safe, and there are multi-use pathways suitable for exploration on horseback or by bicycle. There is also a good-sized car-park.

Right: Low aerial view looking SW to the Marriott's Shaft complex of Basset Mines, South Wheal Frances section. When the mine closed in 1918, it was still the best-equipped shaft in Cornwall: 'new' miners' dry, one of the largest in Cornwall (centre, far left, above track); horizontal winder-engine house (centre, left); boiler house and stack which served all engines (lower centre); compound pumping-engine house (centre, near right); air-compressor house for rock drills (centre, right); capstan house and ore-sorter/stone-breaker base driven by a 16-in Tangye horizontal engine (centre, far right).

View north: the grilled circular collar of Marriott's Shaft (lower left) in front of the 30-ft-high arched beam opening of the pumping-engine house (no bob-wall, the two inverted cylinders powered an under-beam mounted in a slot below them – there are foundations for a second engine, never installed, in this house built for two); boiler house (centre), showing arches for six Lancashire boilers; winding house (right) aligned with the shaft.

Basset Mines pumped an estimated 100 times the weight of ore in wet winters. A big inverted compound (40-in and 80-in) pumping engine was erected at Marriott's Shaft in 1897–8, to replace an 80-in Cornish beam pumping engine destroyed by fire in 1895. It was built by Hathorn Davey & Co at their Sun Lane Works, Leeds. The partner Henry Davey (1843–1929) served his first five years in engineering apprenticeship at the foundry of Nicholls, Matthews & Co in Tavistock. The winder house contained a cross-compound engine made by Holman Bros of Camborne. The bi-conical drum gave a maximum winding speed of 2,000 ft per minute in the shaft.

Looking eastwards from the top of the masonry remnant of the ore-sorter to the side elevation of the compressor house, the taller pumping-engine house and stack behind. Inside the compressor house is a flywheel slot between loadings for a Riedler-type compressor with two-stage air cylinders driven by a Frazer & Chalmers cross-compound horizontal steam engine. This drove up to 30 labour- and time-saving percussive compressed-air-driven rock-drills. The exhaust air from the drills also provided an element of ventilation and cool air in the mine workings. The seven square openings at the base of the wall are 'crow-holes' for man-access to the engine holding-down bolts.

West Basset New Stamps

OS Explorer 104: SW688403

West Basset New Stamps, 300 yd NNE of Carnkie, is one of Cornwall's best-surviving complexes of steam-powered tin stamps and ore-dressing floors. This remarkable site has been conserved and made safe, though heather and low foliage may conceal drainage channels and other 'ankle-traps'. It can be approached via several footpaths, or accessed by the track opposite Wheal Basset Inn, at the eastern end of Lower Carnkie – you can park at Lyle's Shaft engine houses.

It is called West Basset New Stamps, though on the site of North Wheal Basset near Piece (closed 1866, wound up 1872), because the 'old stamps' was so poor that it sold much of its tinstone as ore, not concentrated 'black tin'. From about 1869, ore raised from Thomas's Shaft of West Wheal Basset came here – to old North Wheal Basset Stamps – before upgrading them as West Basset New Stamps in 1875. When Basset Mines Ltd took over, from 1896, ore was brought here (and to Wheal Basset Stamps) by tramway from Marriott's Shaft.

South Wheal Frances 30-in beam whim-engine house, which wound from Pascoe's Shaft, 90 yd NE. The wall on the right of this unusually slim engine house is the far gable of its boiler house, which contained two Cornish boilers. South Frances was the first in Cornwall, from 1860, to permanently use wire rope in place of hemp or chains.

Left: Seemingly complex archaeology on this classic tiered site is simplified from the air: (centre right) engine house for 40-in double-acting stamps-engine designed by Matthew Loam, built by John Hocking at Tuckingmill Foundry, 1875 – note slot at the back of the house, right, for a back-bob to pump dressing-water, and crankshaft loading in front with two lateral slots for twin flywheels which originally powered 32 heads of Cornish stamps on each side, latterly the nearer side being increased to 48; (centre) long rectangular, gabled, Frue-vanner house built for 20 vanners in 1902, driven by a horizontal engine in a house projecting from the lower centre, to deal with sand from the stamps; (lower left) buddle floor containing 14 buddles; (centre left) twin, square buildings formerly containing a double Brunton calciner which roasted off arsenic and sulphides from the vanner concentrates – the stack (upper right) belongs to these calciners and was connected via a flue; (centre far left) sample house. Rag frames and round frames were installed below and to the east in 1903 to recover an estimated 3 tons of slime tin per month that would otherwise be sent downstream to be recovered by tin-streamers on its journey to Portreath. By 1909, almost all Basset Mines' tin ore was burnt and dressed here.

The 'new' Basset counthouse, built after the destruction of the old counthouse by suspected arson in 1891. There was a series of unexplained fires at South Frances in 1894 and 1895 (old Marriott's Shaft 80-in engine), West Basset in 1896 (Thomas's Shaft engine), and Wheal Basset when, it is said among other reasons, tributers' livelihoods were being threatened by the introduction of contract tutwork and other cost-cutting measures leading up to the formation of Basset Mines Ltd. Engine houses of Wheal Uny on the skyline.

Wheal Basset Stamps

OS Explorer 104: SW692398

Wheal Basset occupied a NE–SW-oriented sett, ½ mile long x ¼ mile wide, on the south of the Carnkie–Redruth road and east of Loscombe Road. Its remains are impressive, though the reddish sandy burrows, treated during the 1930s, have been removed. They remained a conspicuous feature on the northern slopes of the Carnmenellis granite, crowned by the 500-ft-high broadcasting and telecommunications mast, until taken away for treatment for their tin content in the early

Left: Striking archaeology at Wheal Basset Stamps comprises, from right to left: stack for the boiler house, which joined the near-side of the engine house (the concrete addition to the single remnant wall, pointing in the direction of the stack, dates from the 1930s when the engine house was used as an ore bin for reworking the burrows); engine house (centre) with extra-width bob-wall built in 1868 for two, side-by-side, 30-in rotary beam engines which eventually drove two rows, each of 48 heads of Cornish stamps, either side of the loading for the crankshafts and common flywheel (the loadings and concrete bases in front of the house are later ones for Californian stamps); Frue vanner house, built on top of the former Wheal Basset dressing floors in 1908. In latter days the stamps were supplied with ore via tramways from Lyle's Shaft (inclined tramway) and from Marriott's Shaft.

1980s. The remnants have been landscaped, and recent conservation and access works here have integrated the site as part of the Great Flat Lode Trail of the Mineral Tramways Project.

Wheal Basset, named after mineral lords the Bassets of Tehidy, is one of several mines which bear the Basset name in their title. It was the richest and most successful mine in the southern part of the Camborne-Redruth Mining District, producing 94,200 tons of 8½-per-cent copper ore and 14,178 tons of black tin between 1815 and 1900. Dividends

Lyle's Shaft, North Wheal Basset, named after principal shareholder, Joseph Lyle, who took the original 1830 lease of this mine in 1842. Within just over 20 years, the mine raised over 30,000 tons of copper ore, at a profit of over £50,000, from steep lodes mostly in the 140-fm-deep killas-filled trough between the Carn Brea and Carnmenellis granites.

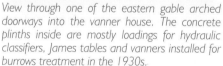

View through one of the eastern gable arched doorways into the vanner house. The concrete plinths inside are mostly loadings for hydraulic classifiers, James tables and vanners installed for burrows treatment in the 1930s.

approached £350,000 on an investment of less than £80,000. In 1855–6, the peak year of Cornish copper production, Wheal Basset ranked third in Cornwall, producing 7,856 tons of copper ore valued at £66,999.

Wheal Basset took over part of the abandoned sett in 1871, including Lyle's Shaft, where in 1879 the surviving pumping-engine house was built in a three-month contract using stone from an abandoned engine house being cleared on nearby Grace's Shaft, and from one lying derelict on South Carn Brea Mine. The engine was a Harvey's of Hayle 80-in pumping engine, the third engine to serve the shaft which was sunk vertically to an eventual depth of 230 fm, intersecting the tin-rich, SE-dipping Great Flat Lode in the 190-fm level by 1885.

to the successful West Wheal Basset, started for copper in 1835, which, 60 years later, employed 300 men, 90 women and 30 boys on the largest sett in what became part of Basset Mines Ltd.

The sturdy dressed-granite structure has contemporary iron reinforcement between which, above the plug-door arch, a granite date-stone proclaims 'AD 1854'. A 60-in pumping engine was working here by January 1855, the shaft named after the company chairman, WA Thomas.

Production of copper ore was at its highest in 1856, when £23,850 was paid in shareholders' dividends. Black tin production reached over 10,000 tons in 1855–91. In 1892, after the mine had been incurring losses for several years, it amalgamated with South Wheal Frances as South Frances United Mines, prior to incorporation as part of Basset Mines Ltd in 1896.

Grenville United Mines

OS Explorer 104: SW668388

Grenville United Mines adds substantially to the Great Flat Lode Trail and a visit should be combined with the adjacent King Edward Mine where interpretation of all things tin is exemplary. The remains of two impressive engine houses stand at Fortescue's Shaft on Newton Moor; the conspicuous engine house and Frue vanner house of Grenville New Stamps stand on the northern slopes of Croft Common, NE of Troon.

West Wheal Basset

OS Explorer 104: SW682397

The solitary bob-wall at Thomas's Shaft, West Wheal Basset – a familiar landmark next to Loscombe Road leading down from Four Lanes, 200 yd east of the Countryman Inn at Piece. It overlooks the shallow valley that leads from Higher Carnkie to Treskillard, once covered in a mile-long run of surface paraphernalia belonging

Grenville New Stamps, built 1891. This low aerial shot shows an almost plan view of the two large flywheel slots in the massive granite masonry crankshaft loading in front of the engine house. Extending to the sides of both flywheels would have been the rotating axles which drove the 136-head battery of Cornish stamps. The depression between the two flywheel slots was for the crank, which was attached by a sweep-rod to the outdoor nose of the bob. The square plinth (top centre) supported an auxiliary bob which pumped water from a shallow shaft to the stamps grates. Remains of two walls of the boiler house, which contained three boilers, can be seen attached to the engine house (bottom). The engine was a 30-in beam whim purchased from nearby South Tolcarne Mine.

Grenville's peak output was in 1894, at 1,006 tons of black tin valued at £41,979. The value was low, however, being attributed to a depression in tin price due to output of 'Straits Tin' doubling between 1887 and 1894.

Fortescue's Shaft, Grenville United Mines. The 90-in pumping-engine house is seen through the plug-doorway of the 28-in whim-engine house, in perfect alignment with the 395-fm-deep shaft named after mineral lord George M Fortescue (1791–1877) of Boconnoc, Lostwithiel. Visible on top of the finely dressed granite bob-wall is the cast-iron soleplate and pair of stools upon which the beam, or bob, of this Harvey & Co engine pivoted, and which pumped 1892–1920. Afterwards it went to New Cook's Kitchen Shaft of South Crofty Mine.

Grenville United Mines was formed in 1906. The original Wheal Grenville sett was granted by Baroness Grenville in 1845. It was an unsuccessful copper mine until the late-1870s, when new management took over and the mine was progressively developed at depth, also incorporating the setts of East Wheal Grenville and South Wheal Grenville. It struck the Great Flat Lode and raised a steadily increasing annual tonnage of tin which placed it among the three richest mines in Cornwall by 1882. When Grenville United Mines formed in 1906, the setts of South Condurrow and part of West Wheal Frances were added. The First World War took 20 per cent of the mine's workforce, and after the armistice high costs combined with an unstable tin price led to the mine being finally abandoned in 1921.

Whim-engine house at Marshall's Shaft, South Condurrow Mine, built in 1881 for a second-hand 26-in whim from West Chiverton Mine, near Zelah. The masonry crankshaft loading in front of the house shows the wide slot for the flywheel and drum (or 'cage') which hauled from Marshall's Shaft, 60 yd to the NE. Ruined walls for the boiler house (single boiler) to right of stack.

South Condurrow Mine

OS Explorer 104: SW661385

Conspicuous on high ground to the west side of Newton Road approaching Troon (just over a mile SE of Camborne) are a pair of recently conserved engine houses at Marshall's Shaft, South Condurrow Mine (later part of Grenville United Mines). There are also substantial remains of a stamps-engine house adjacent to the King Edward Mine site.

South Condurrow Mine started just prior to 1850 on a sett formerly known as Old Tye. By 1859, it was raising small quantities of tin and copper ore by horse-whim. Small tonnages produced until 1870, when tin production leapt due to the erection of new steam stamps. Combined with soaring tin prices, this launched South Condurrow as one of the most consistent dividend-paying mines: totalling around £80,000 by the end of 1886. In 1880, 405 men were employed, 180 underground and 225 on the surface.

Marshall's Shaft pumping-engine house, South Condurrow Mine, was completed in 1887 for a 60-in pumping engine bought from Wheal Jane and erected here, pumping from 1888.

1869 stamps-engine house. Together with new tin floors (long since turned into the King Edward Mine football pitch!), this investment literally paid dividends for the South Condurrow adventurers.

In 1881, sinking commenced at a new shaft, Marshall's Shaft in the new (1875) SW extension of the South Condurrow sett in the western limits of the Great Flat Lode. The mine closed in 1896 due to the low price of tin, and in 1903 the plant was sold to neighbouring Wheal Grenville which also kept the Marshall's Shaft pumping engine at work. The eastern part of South Condurrow was taken over by Camborne Mining School in 1897, being renamed King Edward Mine in the year of his coronation (1901). The greater part of the sett became part of Grenville United Mines in 1906.

King Edward Mine

OS Explorer 104: SW664389

King Edward Mine (KEM) is a mile SE of Camborne. It is a rare example of a relatively complete Cornish mine in terms of its exceptional range of surface features. It is also the former training-school site for the world-famous Camborne School of Mines (CSM), probably making it one of the most surveyed places on earth! KEM hosts an amazing array of tin-dressing equipment – mostly in working order – some being original *in situ*, and some rescued to replace missing equipment. Authentic restoration continues at this mostly volunteer-run site, and it is an essential stop

Aerial view looking NE to King Edward Mine, showing: South Condurrow Mine stamps-engine house (1869, lower left); counthouse and attached smith's shop (about 1870, higher left) with carpenter's shop and miners' dry (1904) opposite; whim-engine house (1869, centre right) with mill buildings (1902–6) and calciner with stack (1904) in front; and the timber-framed and paneled survey office (1897, lower right). The grey patch in the top left of the central square of grass is an 1860s cobbled copper-ore floor.

for understanding the exceptional tin-dressing archaeology of the Great Flat Lode mines.

King Edward Mine occupies the eastern part of South Condurrow Mine, centred on Engine Shaft, which was abandoned in 1890. It was reopened in 1897, and soon developed as a modern, fully operational/training

Holman twin-drum steam-winder, prior to reconstruction of the former winder/compressor house which burnt down in 1957; Engine Shaft whimengine house in the background. The engine was brought into service at KEM in 1908, moved to Castle-an-Dinas Mine (St Columb), where it worked 1942–58; was subsequently moved to Wendron Forge tourist attraction (later Poldark Mine) near Helston, and repatriated to KEM and installed on its original mountings in 2003.

One of two surviving, working, Cornish round frames. In 1974, the Trevithick Society rescued the remains of two round frames from a tin-stream works at Tolgarrick in Tuckingmill. One was carefully re-erected (utilizing parts of the two) in exactly the position where King Edward's original round frame once stood. KEM built one of the first newly designed tin mills in Cornwall to utilize newly invented equipment such as Frue vanners and shaking tables. Original equipment remaining includes the only full-size working set of Californian Stamps in Europe, installed here in 1901.

mine run by CSM, an amalgamation of the Redruth, Penzance and Camborne mining schools. It was named King Edward Mine in 1901 on the accession of King Edward VII.

KEM regularly produced tin until the First World War, when work was suspended. Operations resumed in 1920, but the mine was forced to close a year later when Grenville United Mines closed and the interconnected mines flooded; in fact KEM had no pump as water simply drained from the 400-ft-deep workings straight into Grenville. At this time, underground training facilities were transferred to higher, dry and shallow workings at Great Condurrow Mine, adjacent to the north. In 1974, CSM moved their mineral-processing training facilities to the new site in Pool, and in 1987 a volunteer group was set up to conserve and enhance the site. It continues to go from strength to strength.

Wheal Uny

OS Explorer 104: SW695407

This 1880 26-in rotative whim-engine house served Hind's Shaft, Wheal Uny, just over 50 yd to the north (away from the camera). Hind's was vertical to the 150-fm level, and on the underlie to the 244-fm level. It was the deepest shaft on the sett and worked the Great Flat Lode.

Finely dressed granite masonry in the bob-wall of the 70-in pumping-engine house at Hind's Shaft, built 1869–70. The engine was originally manufactured by St Austell Foundry in 1853 for Great Hewas Mine (St Mewan). It was sold in 1860, and re-erected at Tywarnhayle Mine at the eastern end of the St Agnes Mining District, where its house survives. It was purchased in 1869 for Wheal Uny, and worked from 1874 to 1893, being sold in the latter year, with five other engines on the mine, for a mere scrap value of £1,425.

The pair of engine houses at Wheal Uny forms a prominent landmark on high ground immediately east of Church Coombe, just under a mile SSW of Redruth. The mine, whose western boundary is the stream in the coombe, can be accessed by several different footpaths which converge at the site. Wheal Uny also marks the NE end of the outcrop of the Great Flat Lode (named for its unusually shallow dip of around 45° SE), extending from here to just beyond South Condurrow Mine at Troon, a remarkable strike of 3 miles.

Wheal Uny first worked for copper in several steep and near-vertical lodes in overlying killas. Later it mined tin from the Great Flat Lode, in killas close to the granite contact down to the 193-fm level where it enters granite. Wheal Uny was active from at least 1800, and undoubtedly exceeded recorded output as copper, and some tin, were produced intermittently up to mid-century. By 1840, for example, Wheal Uny already possessed a large stamping capacity on its tin floors, and became part of Redruth Consols, being worked for copper by the Fox family of Falmouth 1846–8. Over 2,800 tons of copper ore were produced, mostly 1854–65, and 7,814 tons of black tin 1853–93.

Regarding stamping capacity, during the 1830s and early 1840s, a peculiarity of the mine was its succession of a dozen or more sets of waterwheel stamps fed from a pumping engine which drew water to surface and fed the highest part of the floors, the mine water thus cascading over the wheels downhill. These were up for sale in 1843, and when Wheal Uny restarted in 1851. Tin exceeded copper in importance before the end of the decade, though the mine still did not pay costs. By 1870, 250 people were employed, but after 1884 output crashed, and the mine closed again in 1885. It was restarted in 1887, though Hind's (sump at 214 fm below adit) was not forked until 1888. Final closure came in 1893.

Wheal Peevor

OS Explorer 104: SW707443

Wheal Peevor is located about 175 yd NW of Radnor Farm, on the western flank of North Downs, about 1½ miles NE of Redruth. Recent (2005–7) conservation, safety and access works to this 12-acre site include a trail which takes in a considerable

Looking north across Wheal Peevor, with its aligned trio of conserved engine houses (left to right: stamps, pumping, whim), arsenic calciners and stack (bottom left). Heath-covered burrows vividly illustrate a pattern in the landscape that is clear from the air: the general ENE–WSW strike of the killas-hosted lodes at Peevor (extending into the West Peevor sett) which, indeed, is the predominant trend throughout the Central Mining District. Surface burrows of Little North Downs Mine, a copper mine which commenced work during the early eighteenth century and produced nearly 30,000 tons of copper ore from 1815 to 1871, can be seen (top left), showing the parallel lode trend of this adjacent sett.

number of features of interest, including access to the conspicuous aligned trio of engine houses visible from the A30 trunk road, grilled shafts, ore floors and arsenic calciners. There is a small parking area at the eastern end of the site and the mine remains,

Low aerial view of the stamps-engine house at Wheal Peevor, completed in 1876 at a cost of £223, photographed following conservation 131 years later. The 32-in engine and 48-head set of stamps came from Basset & Grylls Mine, Wendron. The concrete remains to the right date from a 1911–18 reworking for wolfram and tin: base for stone crusher (top); pier loadings for Californian stamps (centre); round buddles (bottom).

set in colourful heathland, make for a pleasant couple of hours exploration.

Wheal Peevor originally mined copper along with its famously rich neighbor, North Downs, where there were Newcomen engines draining rich copper deposits (*Sherborne Mercury* in 1760 lists 'five fire engines'). The Fox family of Falmouth and their friends the Williams family of Gwennap had interests in North Downs, and this spurred the commencement of the Portreath Tramroad in the early years of the nineteenth century, at first linking North Downs with Portreath Harbour which they leased from Basset of Tehidy. Peevor's heyday, however, was its deeper development for tin, which commenced in 1871 in the midst of the 1870–72 'Great Tin Boom', with black tin prices of over £80 per ton – the highest since 1810, and almost double that of the 1840s. The 3,280 tons of black tin recorded 1872–89 brought profits, although the price of black tin dropped from £87 per ton in 1872 to £53 per ton in 1889, with its sharpest fall after 1873. This was a time when new tin bonanzas swept Australia (Queensland, New South Wales and Tasmania) and the ore, much of it alluvial, filled the holds of wool clippers, with most of it destined for Cornish smelting houses until their own were set up towards the end of the decade. In 1878, Peevor, among 13 profitable Cornish tin mines in that year, still managed a dividend of £2,250. The three beam engines were put up for auction in 1896, attracting a maximum bid of £435.

The largest engine house, in the centre of the trio, before conservation, showing where the rear gable collapsed in the 1990s. Built in 1872 for an old Harvey's of Hayle 60-in pumping engine with hollow-work (lattice) bob, moved with the masonry of its engine house from Great North Downs copper mine. It served Sir Frederick's Engine Shaft (Sir Frederick M Williams, was MP of Tregullow; he inherited some of Cornwall's major mine shareholdings from his father, and took a major share of this undertaking in 1872). The Great County Adit (another venture with which the Williams family are associated) drained the mine to 50 fm.

Wheal Peevor 24-in whim-engine house, its stack showing the top elevation of decoratively coursed brickwork, prior to conservation. Built in 1872 for an engine which, together with its house, was relocated from Great North Downs Mine. It is aligned to draw from Sir Frederick's Engine Shaft (110 fm, now grilled on this accessible site).

West Wheal Peevor

Carn Brea Mine

OS Explorer 104: SW705441

OS Explorer 104: SW674408

The 20-in stamps-engine house, about 300 yd north of Radnor Road, glimpsed by west-bound travellers on the A30 a mile NNE of Redruth. The ivy-covered flywheel loading and site of the stamps is clearly visible in front (left) of the engine house; the dressing floors were on the adjacent (southern) slope of a shallow valley. West Peevor was started on the back of its successful neighbour Wheal Peevor in 1875, sharing some of its lodes and directors. The stamps engine and a pumping engine were erected in 1882. It produced over 240 tons of black tin in 1882–3, then struggled on unsuccessfully until abandonment in 1893. A 50-in pumping-engine house survives on Michell's Shaft, 150 yd to the east, its higher elevation truncated by prospecting in the shaft in 1968: the contractor who lowered the top half of the engine house, which was to be used as the mine office, threw the rubble down the shaft which was to be reopened.

The stepped stack and stamps-engine house built in 1837 for a 32-in engine driving 40 heads of Cornish stamps (70 by 1842, 84 by 1851, 96 by 1859), at the western end of Carn Brea Mine, which ran from Tregajorran almost to Carn Brea village – among the largest setts in Cornwall.

Carn Brea combined four old copper mines: Wheal Druid, Barncoose, Tregajorran and Wheal Fanny. It started in 1832, and was soon the most productive copper mine in Cornwall, employing over 1,000 people. It had 11 engines, and soon paid over £273,000 in dividends against initial calls of £1,500 – mostly from copper. By 1837, it was raising tin from the Wheal Fanny section, so steam-stamps were installed. By the mid-1850s, tin returned more than copper. Overall, 1833–96, production exceeded 237,000 tons of copper ore, almost 30,000 tons of black tin, and several thousand tons of arsenic.

Pednandrea Mine

OS Explorer 104: SW703420

The 'telescoped' stack, built in 1824, is a landmark at the eastern end of the town (pednandrea = head of the town). It stands near Wesley Street, 170 yd east of Redruth railway station, next to the mine's counthouse (top right). The

stack was originally 145 ft high. The engine for which it was constructed worked for only three years. The mine workings lie beneath the town; its surface remains have been mostly built over.

Pednandrea produced tin, and copper, from at least the early eighteenth century, and was one of the largest tin producers in the Redruth area. Other ores encountered included cobalt, uranium, lead and tungsten.

Great Condurrow Mine

OS Explorer 104: SW662393

The pumping-engine house of Great Condurrow Mine stands on the southern ridge of Carn Entral, less than a mile SE of Camborne. It overlooks Condurrow Road at Higher Condurrow, forming a landmark when viewed from the south between Troon and Four Lanes. It was built in 1906 for an 80-in pumping engine at the 270-fm Woolf's Shaft (later Neame's, after the Chairman of Condurrow Mines). The engine has an interesting history and leaves a legacy of other houses still to be seen in Cornwall: it was originally made in 1868 by Harvey's of Hayle as Batters' Engine for West Chiverton Mine, near Zelah, where the engine house survives. When West Chiverton closed in 1882, Harvey's bought it, putting it in store until 1899, when it was sold to Gwennap United Mines to serve Garland's Shaft; the remains of its engine house survive there too. In 1907, it restarted as Neame's Engine, being finally scrapped in 1916.

Great Condurrow worked in the Carn Brea granite mass from the early nineteenth century; the lodes contained both tin and copper: 1856–65 production is recorded at 30,495 tons of copper ore and 2,030 tons of black tin, plus a little arsenic and pyrite; employees numbered 380 at its peak. It was reopened, unsuccessfully, 1906–14 as Condurrow Mines.

North Treskerby Mine

OS Explorer 104: SW723452

Above: The stamps-engine house of North Treskerby Mine, authentically converted, standing next to the Scorrier–Porthtowan road at Wheal Rose.

Right: Though strictly in St Agnes parish, this graceful engine house, a landmark visible from the A30 and the mainline railway, is on the southern flank of a hill about ½ mile north of Scorrier. It housed an 80-in pumping engine, designed by Michell of Redruth and supplied ex-Wheal Falmouth & Sperries Mine, Kea, by the dealer Lanyon of Redruth in 1872. It was erected at Doctor's Shaft in the eastern part of the sett, where it started in 1877. Output 1859–82 was 19,270 tons of copper ore and 150 tons of black tin, together with some arsenic (ore and soot) and pyrite.

Trevoole Mine (West Grenville Mine)

OS Explorer 104: SW639372

The engine house and two stacks of Trevoole Mine, otherwise West Grenville Mine, is a familiar landmark to travellers on the B3303 Camborne to Praze-an-Beeble road, 2 miles SSW of Camborne. As Trevoole Mine, named after Trevoole hamlet, it was active in 1827 and again 1856–62, producing 3,400 tons of copper ore and a little black tin. The engine houses were built in 1857, and under the name of West Grenville were working in 1887–91, when a 70-in engine was erected.

Illustrated Glossary

adit: a tunnel, usually driven from the base of a cliff or a deep valley, and gently inclined to facilitate natural drainage and access to mine workings. The term 'deep adit' was used for the lowest point at which a mine could be drained without the aid of pumps. Adits were also used for haulage, exploration and ventilation.

Adit level, Polmear Beach, Charlestown

adventurer: a shareholder in a mine. An 'adventure' was the Cornish term for working a mine.

bal: Cornish word for a mine. In medieval times a group of tin workings was known as a ball, e.g. Godolphin Ball.

balance bob: a counterweighted lever attached to pump rods in a **shaft**. This was used to offset the great weight of the wooden pump rods, that extended the depth of the shaft, and they were mounted both on the surface and underground.

Balance Bob, Taylor's Shaft, East Pool & Agar Mine, Pool

beam engine: a type of steam-engine used in pumping and for winding and crushing ore. The power from the steam cylinder was transferred via a piston and rocking beam (or **bob**) to pumps in the **shaft**. For winding and crushing, the motion of the beam was connected via a sweep-rod to a flywheel which provided rotational energy and steadied the rotation of a crankshaft.

Michell's Whim, East Pool Mine, Pool

black tin: the ore-mineral cassiterite (tin oxide) crushed and concentrated on the mine's **dressing floors**. A tin mine's recorded production, sold to smelting houses, is recorded in tons of black tin.

bob: a Cornish term for a beam of a beam engine. The bob commonly pivoted on the **bob-wall**. Early bobs were made of wood; later ones were commonly made of cast iron or, more rarely, lattice-work wrought iron. Angle bobs were used to change direction from horizontal to vertical motion.

bob-plat: the timber platform that extended from the front of an **engine house** to access the outer end of the **bob**.

Bob plat, Taylor's Shaft, East Pool & Agar Mine, Pool

bob-wall: the strongest wall at the front of an **engine house**.

Bob wall, West Basset Mine, Carnkie

Brunton calciner: see **calciner**.

buddle: a device which uses water and gravity to separate heavy cassiterite from lighter waste; this process of concentrating the ore took place either at a mine or in a tin **streamworks**. By the mid-nineteenth century, buddles were usually circular pits (con-

vex or concave) where ore from the **stamps** was fed into the centre or side of the pit. Rotating brushes prevented riddles forming in the concentrate which formed nearest the inlet point.

Tin dressing buddle, King Edward Mine, Troon

bunchy: term for a **lode** which tended to have clusters of ore minerals divided by barren areas, often leading to feast or famine for miners.

burning house: see **calciner**.

burrow: a heap of mine waste, also known as a dump or spoil heap. May contain primary waste such as coarse rock from **shaft**-sinking and cross-cutting, waste from initial ore-sorting, and finer wastes such as sand and silt from ore-dressing.

*Burrows, Cargoll Mine,
St Newlyn East*

Buss shaking tables: one of several designs of **shaking tables** which use water and gravity for concentrating crushed tin ore. The deck and shaking motion mimic the technique of the prospector with his gold pan.

calciner: originally a furnace in which tin concentrate was roasted to drive off sulphides and arsenic; also known as a **burning house**. Later, in the nineteenth century, arsenic was recovered as a by-product and then, with increasing demand, arsenic ore (arsenopyrite = arsenic and iron sulphide, often called **mispickel** by miners) was calcined to produce the arsenic oxide, subsequently refined. The mechanically-powered Brunton calciner, introduced in the mid-nineteenth century, operated on a continuous rather than a batch basis.

Calciner, Tolgus Valley, Redruth

Calciner, Carn Praunter, St Just

Clwyd cap: a distinctive form of capping mine **shafts** with conical metal mesh, popular in the 1980s, but no longer favoured.

*Clwyd cap, Perran St George
Mine, St Agnes*

counthouse: the account house or mine office, often incorporating accommodation for the captain or purser.

*Counthouse, Botallack Mine,
St Just*

*Counthouse, Phoenix Mine,
Linkinhorne*

crosscourse: a mineral vein, economic or not, which runs across or through principal **lodes**, often at right-angles. Cross courses were often filled with clay and sometimes referred to as a Fluccan.

dressing floor: the processing and concentration of ore was known as dressing, and was carried out on a dressing floor: an often extensive area on the surface of a mine where the processing and concentration of ore took place.

Dressing floor, Wheal Kitty, St Agnes

drive: a tunnel excavated along a **lode**; also known as a heading. Ore was extracted from **stopes** above and below a drive.

dry: a miners' change-house used before and after going underground. In the later nineteenth century, some were heated by steam pipes connected to engine boilers, and also provided with hot water and, rarely, baths.

Dry, Harriet's Shaft, Dolcoath Mine, Camborne

engine house: a building designed to contain steam, gas, oil or electric engines on a mine. In the case of a **beam engine**, the engine house formed a major part of the structural framework of the engine and was strongly constructed, hence their enduring survival.

Fortescue's whim-engine house, Wheal Grenville, Troon

engine pond: reservoir used to supply clean water to a steam engine. Often mine water pumped from underground was too acidic and

Engine pond, Pearce's Shaft, South Caradon Mine, St Cleer

corroded the boilers, so **leats** often brought water from some considerable distance. They were also used for condensing water.

flat-rod: reciprocating iron, wood or chain 'rods' that run on a horizontal plane (rather than vertical), used to transfer power from a steam engine or waterwheel to a remote location.

flue: a masonry or sometimes iron conduit connecting a furnace to a **stack**. Also a term used for an arsenic labyrinth.

froth flotation: an ore-dressing technique first devised in the 1890s which separated ore minerals from waste using oils or chemicals and air bubbles which created a froth to which certain minerals tended to adhere.

Frue vanner house: building which housed Frue vanners. See **vanner**.

Vanner house, Grenville United Mines, Troon

gunnies: see **stope**.

headframe: the tall construction set over a winding **shaft**

Headframe, Wheal Concorde, Mount Hawke

which carried the sheave wheels over which the winding ropes ran. Headframes usually contained ore bins or ore chutes to allow the broken rock in the skips or kibbles to be tipped into trams at surface.

James table: see **shaking table**.

kieve: an old English word for a tub, used by Cornish tin-dressers as the name of a barrel which further concentrated ore from **buddles** or tables. The sides of the barrel are flared slightly upwards and, half-filled with water, the fines (fine tin ore mixed with waste) are agitated and left to settle with the heavier ore at the bottom.

killas: Cornish geological term for sedimentary rock, often metamorphosed by intruded granite or altered by mineralization.

launder: a wooden or steel trough used to carry water or other liquids; often used to feed water or finely divided material in suspension around a **dressing floor**.

leat: an artificial watercourse, built to carry a supply of water to a mine.

Launder and leat, Dolcoath Mine, Camborne

Leat, Levant Mine, St Just

level: a horizontal tunnel. Also a specific horizon at a certain depth in a mine e.g. 24-fm level.

lode: a mineral vein, or linear zone of mineralization, commonly near-vertical in Cornish mines as they usually occupied normal faults.

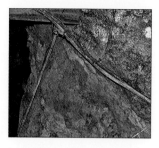

Lode, Wheal Roots (Poldark Mine), Wendron

magazine: an explosives (gun-powder or dynamite) store, commonly circular with a conical roof, sometimes with additional enclosing walls to contain an accidental explosion.

Magazine, Old Shepherd's Mine, St Newlyn East

man-engine: a machine for raising and lowering miners in a mine **shaft**. Men rode the engine by stepping from sollars (platforms in the shaft) to steps on the rod. When the engine stroke was completed, they stepped on to the next sollar and repeated this action until their journey was completed.

mine captain: manager of a mine. There were both underground and surface captains on larger mines.

mineral lord: the owner of the mineral rights, not necessarily the landowner.

mispickel: miners' term for arsenopyrite, the common sulphide of arsenic and iron, and the principal ore of arsenic.

openworks: a mine, rather like a quarry, open to surface and worked open-cast. The term 'bunny' was applied in the St Just mining district.

Openworks, The Bunny, Botallack, St Just

ore floor: an area, often cobbled, used for storage of ore prior to sale or transport. Can also be a **dressing floor**.

Ore floor, South Caradon Mine, St Cleer

plug-door: the doorway in the **bob-wall** of an **engine house**, at the engine driver's floor level.

sett: the legal boundary granted to a mine for mineral extraction. *Also* a stone block used to support a tramway rail: parallel rows of setts performed the same function as sleepers, except they were longitudinal as opposed to perpendicular, allowing a horse to walk along the centre hauling wagons.

shaft: usually a vertical or near-vertical tunnel sunk to give access underground and for ventilation. Often crooked and could be diagonal.

Shaft, Wheal Cock, St Just

shaking table: uses water and gravity to concentrate crushed tin ore. The deck and shaking motion mimic the technique of the prospector with a gold pan.

Shaking tables, King Edward Mine, Troon

stack: a chimney stack used to carry away smoke or fumes from boilers, furnaces and **calciners**. Often attached to the wall of an **engine house**, or solitary on higher ground and situated at the end of a **flue**.

Stacks, site of Wheal Raven, Redruth

stamps: a machine for crushing ore to fine sand. Originally small stamping mills were powered by waterwheels, but later much larger ones were powered by steam engines. Vertical wooden or iron posts

Cornish stamps (from Nancledra), Geevor Mine, St Just

(lifters) carried heavy iron heads that were sequentially lifted and dropped by a series of cams mounted on a revolving axle on to the ore beneath. There were various types, such as Cornish, Californian and pneumatic.

stockwork: a structurally controlled swarm of ore-bearing veins.

stope: an area from which ore is extracted, usually between levels. When worked out, and not back-filled, they usually

Stope, South Crofty Mine, Pool

leave narrow, deep and elongated caverns that reflect the former position of the **lode**. Where open to the surface, they are termed **gunnises** or coffens.

streamworks: an area worked by shallow excavation for geologically redeposited tin ore. Deposits often followed river valleys, and **leats** and reservoirs were constructed to divert and use water in their operation.

strike: the orientation of a mineral vein where it intersects a horizontal plane, usually shown as a line on a map. Many tin and copper **lodes** had a roughly east-west direction, whereas silver-lead lodes often had a roughly north-south direction.

tailings: the waste sand and slime from a mine **dressing floor** which was considered valueless, or at least not worth further working. Many fine metallic minerals were lost, however, especially from the earlier **tin floors**, hence the large number of tin recovery works in valleys downstream from large mines.

tin floor: a tin **dressing floor** is where **black tin** was concentrated from the ore which included lighter waste. Tin floors were usually sited on sloping ground due to the methods which principally used water and gravity. Their remains often show a terraced or stepped form.

Round frame, King Edward Mine, Troon

tin-streamer: someone who either worked ancient, geologically redeposited, tin-bearing gravels in a **streamworks**; or worked in a tin recovery works which recovered fine tin from waste 'slimes' discharged from mine **dressing floors**.

tramway: a lightly laid railway used to haul mineral and materials underground and at surface.

tribute: a miner working on tribute (a tributer) was paid at an agreed percentage of the value of ore he raised from a measured area of **stope** (a pitch) in a given time. He gained his contract for a pitch at a Dutch auction held by the **mine captain**.

tutwork: piecework, whereby a miner was paid so much per fm of tunnel driven or **lode** stoped.

vanner: a **Frue vanner**, devised in America in 1874, was a mechanically driven, laterally vibrated, inclined endless rubber belt. A pulp of fine cassiterite (tin ore) direct from the **stamps** was washed by water and concentrated by relative density. A Vanning shovel was used to test the relative concentration of ore in a sample of finely crushed ore. Water was used together with a hand-motion of the shovel which separated cassiterite from waste.

wheal: Cornish word for work, or working, as applied to a mine.

whim: a machine for hoisting ore and rock, materials, water and miners in a mine. These could be powered by horses, waterwheels or steam engines (later electricity). Rope, chains or iron/steel cable passed from a winding drum over the

Whim, East Pool Mine, Pool

sheave wheels of a **headframe** and down the **shaft**.

winder stack: see **stack**.